Thieves & Kings

Thieves & Kings Volume One copyright © 2005 Mark Oakley.
All rights reserved.

Published by,
I Box Publishing, P.O. Box 2414,
Wolfville, Nova Scotia, B4P 2S3 Canada

www.iboxpublishing.com

ISBN 0-9681025-0-6

Printed in Canada

I Box Publishing welcomes any comments or questions at the
above addresses, and may publish/answer them in the letters
pages of the on-going comic book series, available at finer comic
shops everywhere.

First Printing 1996
Fourth Printing 2005

Reminiscence.   by Ed Green.

It seems like a long time ago. John, Dan, Mark and myself. Grade 12 Creative Writing with Mrs. Eynon. That was where we could find relief from the stultifying effects of Physics, Calculus and Accounting. That was where we could recharge our atrophying brain cells. I believe it was also where the appellation "M'Oak" originated. —We turned those 50 minute classes into our own private bull sessions, (and I do mean bull), perverting our assignments to meet the twisted needs of our creative appetites. We transformed them into great adolescent literary jam sessions, riffing, improvising and soloing, playing with and against each other, hitting the odd bum note, but usually locking in the groove. Mostly we had ourselves a ball. And sometimes got turfed out of class. For the rest of us it was a chance to cut loose, but for Mark it may have been something more. If this wasn't the place where Mark the writer, the storyteller, first cut his teeth, it was certainly the place where he first displayed and refined his chops in public.

About a year later I lost track of Mark. It seems he had carefully calculated that he had comfortably passed all the classes he required for his diploma, and rather than "playing out the string," to use a sports analogy, (Mark never uses sports analogies), he decided to dedicate himself to other, nobler pursuits.

So, just like that, he stopped coming to school. In the middle of the year.

This kind of surprised me.

It was three years before I saw Mark again. I heard things. He was busy doing some traveling, a little work, a bit of art college. And a stint at one of the biggest animation houses in North America.

That last one didn't surprise me at all.

One freezing spring afternoon I finally ran into Mark again, (just outside the *Dragon Lady Comic Shop*, natch). He was with his old pal Carson, *I Box Publishing*'s resident traffic manager/subscription poobah and all-around unsung hero of *T&K*. What was I up to? Not much. And you Mark? "Er, I'm publishing my own comics."

Hmm. I thought back to that old Toronto indy-comics pioneer from the early 1980's, *The Mundane Adventures of Dishman.* It was a satirical, b&w Xeroxed eight-pager that was available at local comic shops for 25 cents. When it came out. When you could find it. How quaint, I thought. Mark is going to photocopy some doodles he scratched out in his basement.

Nope.

This baby was a full-size comic. With a full-colour cover. Printed, bound and shipped by a big out-of-town printer. Internationally distributed. Not only that, but Mark had already mapped out the storyline for the entire 100 issue run, which would keep him busy behind his art desk for, oh, the next 16 years or so. Bi-monthly, of course.

This kind of surprised me.

It shouldn't have really though. I've known Mark since before forever and he always had the ability to blow people away with his stuff. He never made a loud or pretentious display of his talents. He would just quietly go over into a corner and come back with a story or picture to make your eyes pop out. The only difference today is that he's combining the story and art. No big deal. For Mark that is. For the rest of us a very big deal indeed.

A lot has changed over the years since that creative writing class. *Dishman* is gone. Mrs. Eynon is dead. And they're tearing down the high school. But it's nice to know that there are some things you can still count on. Like Rubel the Thief fighting his way through all manner of fantastic and astonishing travails on his ascent to his ultimate destiny. Like Varkias' flitting, puckish charm, cajoling and consoling his special friend every step of the way. And like the omniscient presence of the Shadow Lady, dispassionately surveying the magical tableaux unfolding before her eyes. And your eyes. Every sixty days. Some things don't change.

And if you know M'Oak, that is no surprise.

Ed Green
Toronto, Canada
August 1996

Thank You:

Brian
Daniel
Paul
Ed
Carson and the Courts Three
Ron
Templeton
Sim
Duffel
Emino & Smith
Larson
Crease
Moses
Paul & Niko
And of Course, My Family

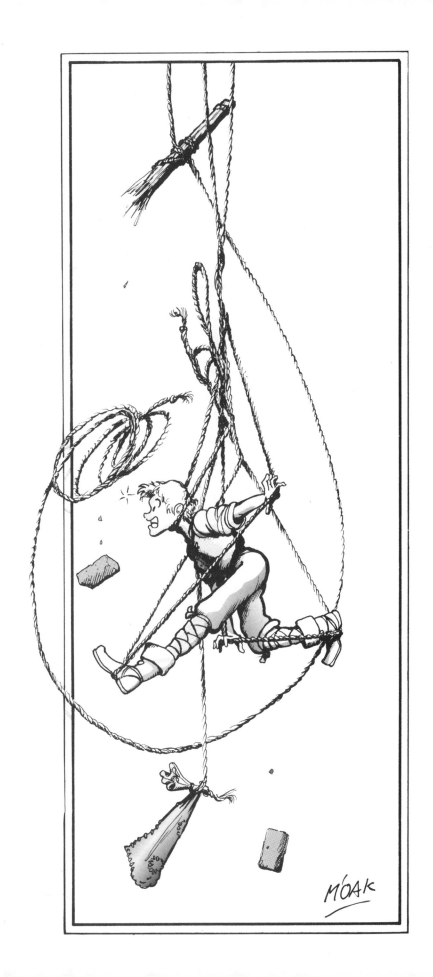

Chapter 1

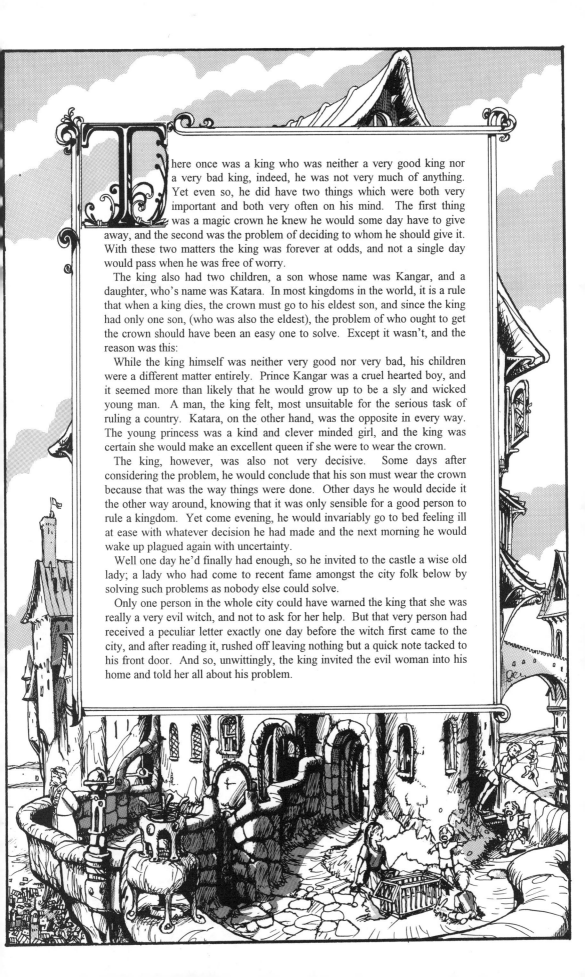

There once was a king who was neither a very good king nor a very bad king, indeed, he was not very much of anything. Yet even so, he did have two things which were both very important and both very often on his mind. The first thing was a magic crown he knew he would some day have to give away, and the second was the problem of deciding to whom he should give it. With these two matters the king was forever at odds, and not a single day would pass when he was free of worry.

The king also had two children, a son whose name was Kangar, and a daughter, who's name was Katara. In most kingdoms in the world, it is a rule that when a king dies, the crown must go to his eldest son, and since the king had only one son, (who was also the eldest), the problem of who ought to get the crown should have been an easy one to solve. Except it wasn't, and the reason was this:

While the king himself was neither very good nor very bad, his children were a different matter entirely. Prince Kangar was a cruel hearted boy, and it seemed more than likely that he would grow up to be a sly and wicked young man. A man, the king felt, most unsuitable for the serious task of ruling a country. Katara, on the other hand, was the opposite in every way. The young princess was a kind and clever minded girl, and the king was certain she would make an excellent queen if she were to wear the crown.

The king, however, was also not very decisive. Some days after considering the problem, he would conclude that his son must wear the crown because that was the way things were done. Other days he would decide it the other way around, knowing that it was only sensible for a good person to rule a kingdom. Yet come evening, he would invariably go to bed feeling ill at ease with whatever decision he had made and the next morning he would wake up plagued again with uncertainty.

Well one day he'd finally had enough, so he invited to the castle a wise old lady; a lady who had come to recent fame amongst the city folk below by solving such problems as nobody else could solve.

Only one person in the whole city could have warned the king that she was really a very evil witch, and not to ask for her help. But that very person had received a peculiar letter exactly one day before the witch first came to the city, and after reading it, rushed off leaving nothing but a quick note tacked to his front door. And so, unwittingly, the king invited the evil woman into his home and told her all about his problem.

he witch listened to him very carefully, clucking her tongue and saying things which made her sound sympathetic and wise. Once the king had finished with his tale, the witch nodded in thought and then told him what she thought he ought to do. The king's face lit up; the things she told him seemed very wise indeed. He thanked her grandly and immediately set out to follow the advice he had been given.

As soon as it was dark, the king stole off into the woods with the crown tucked beneath his cloak, and there in the forest, he hid it in a place where it would be difficult to find. What he did not know, however, was that the witch had followed him to see where that hiding place would be, for she meant to come back the next day and take it for herself.

What the *witch* did not know, however, was that wicked young Kangar, had crept up to the key hole to hear all the things she and his father spoke that afternoon, and he had guessed what she was up to. So when the witch secretly followed the king into the woods, the wicked young prince secretly followed the witch. After his father had hidden the crown and gone off back home, and after the witch had seen where he had hidden it and crept away as well, prince Kangar took the crown and put it in a different place entirely so that only *he* would know where it was. Then he went back home as well, feeling very wicked and very clever indeed!

What *none* of them knew, however, was that a young thief, being rather surprised to see so many people creeping about in the woods, had decided to follow along as well. When he saw that a golden crown was the cause of all the fuss, he too became interested. And so, after the young prince had gone off back home, the thief took up the crown from where it had been hidden and skipped away with a whistle, singing, "Oh what a find I've found!"

he very next day, early in the morning, the king got up in an unusually good mood and he called all of the people together to announce a decision he had made. As the king rarely made any decisions, this was seen as an important event, so people came from all over to hear what he would say. When all had assembled, the king explained that he had hidden his crown somewhere in the woods, and that he was sending his daughter and his son out by themselves to look for it. He declared that whoever first held the crown up above his or her head would be the next ruler of the kingdom!

There was much excitement and bother made over this, and those who hadn't gone to hear the king's announcement soon heard about it nonetheless. It was agreed to be outrageous that the king should do such a thing. Such things were simply not done, and if they were they always led to trouble! —King's oldest sons were supposed to become rulers. Not their younger daughters. And since prince Kangar was both the oldest child and a boy, and since his sister Katara was neither, all of this nonsense about crowns being hidden in forests seemed all the more irregular.

When the trumpets sounded to announce the start of the contest, all the people of the city came out to watch as the prince and princess passed. And because they all thought they liked prince Kangar best, they cheered him on as he marched brightly by. They did not do so for Katara. Instead, they whispered unkind things and they all looked at her in such a way that even though she couldn't hear their murmurs, she still knew what they thought. But Katara was not the sort to sulk. She was, after all, a princess. She held her shoulders straight and her gaze firm as she marched. The crowd did not like this; nobody likes it when the one you are sneering at only gets stronger for it. So instead of just murmuring, they started to boo and hiss as well.

Unfortunately, even the strongest people can still feel wretched when everybody hates them, and Katara was no different. Indeed, being booed and hissed at by thousands of adults is all the more terrible when you are only eleven years old. By the time she and her brother reached the edge of the forest Katara didn't care very much at all about crowns or contests. All she really wanted to do was to find a quiet place where she could sit and feel miserable.

The forest that day had more than just the prince and princess within it. There was also the witch. She had gone out that day as well to take the crown. It was her intent to take it from where it had been hidden and go back into the city and hold it high over her own head and declare that since *she* had found it, she must also become the next queen. –Had not the king himself declared that such must be the case? He had done!

This had been her plan all along, but of course, when she went back to the place she had seen it hidden, she found the crown missing and knew immediately that something had gone wrong with her plan. Frustrated, but not daunted, she swore that she would do her best to set things right, (which really meant that she would set things wrong), and she swept off back to the city to figure out how best to do it.

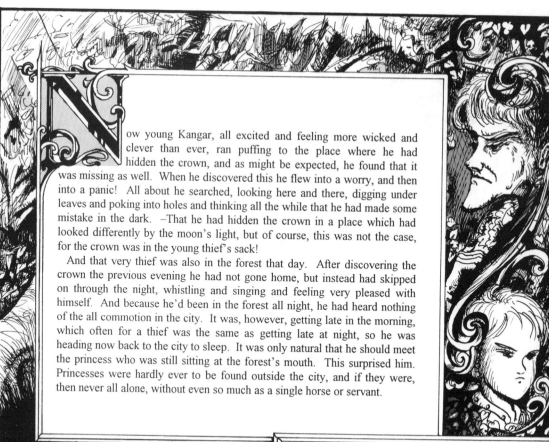

ow young Kangar, all excited and feeling more wicked and clever than ever, ran puffing to the place where he had hidden the crown, and as might be expected, he found that it was missing as well. When he discovered this he flew into a worry, and then into a panic! All about he searched, looking here and there, digging under leaves and poking into holes and thinking all the while that he had made some mistake in the dark. —That he had hidden the crown in a place which had looked differently by the moon's light, but of course, this was not the case, for the crown was in the young thief's sack!

And that very thief was also in the forest that day. After discovering the crown the previous evening he had not gone home, but instead had skipped on through the night, whistling and singing and feeling very pleased with himself. And because he'd been in the forest all night, he had heard nothing of the all commotion in the city. It was, however, getting late in the morning, which often for a thief was the same as getting late at night, so he was heading now back to the city to sleep. It was only natural that he should meet the princess who was still sitting at the forest's mouth. This surprised him. Princesses were hardly ever to be found outside the city, and if they were, then never all alone, without even so much as a single horse or servant.

With his curiosity piqued, he stepped from the trees and asked her what she was all about, which was a very bold thing for him to do. People are supposed to kneel before princesses, or at least lower their heads in respect, neither of which he did. Worse still, common folk are never supposed to speak to royalty unless they are spoken to first. Thieves, however, do not have to worry about things like that, and so he didn't.

But Katara saw that his eyes were kind, and since she was feeling lonely for kindness, she told him all about what had happened to her; about how the crown was hidden in the forest, and how she and her brother had been sent to find it. She told him also, (with narrowed eyes), that she had a very strong feeling that her brother was somehow cheating. —Except it didn't really matter, because nobody wanted her to find the crown anyway. Nobody liked *her* very much.

The young thief's heart was wrung by her words, and he was so happy to have the chance to do a good deed for a princess that he immediately took the crown from his sack and held it up high into the sunlight for her to see. She gasped when she saw it, and he bowed deeply and laid it at her feet.

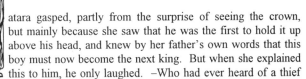

Katara gasped, partly from the surprise of seeing the crown, but mainly because she saw that he was the first to hold it up above his head, and knew by her father's own words that this boy must now become the next king. But when she explained this to him, he only laughed. —Who had ever heard of a thief becoming a king? And why should he want such a thing when everything in the world was already his to take?

Why indeed? Still, Katara knew that there was no getting around it. Such matters involving king's decisions and royal crowns were not to be taken lightly. And since they both felt that Katara's father, (as well as all the people), would be most perplexed to discover that the crown was to go to somebody who wasn't even related to the royal family, the princess and the thief both sat down in thought.

As Katara was a clever girl, and as a good thief is never short of a good idea, between them a solution was quickly found. With the thief's knife, Katara cut forth from her tresses a lock of strawberry hair, and upon it the thief swore himself to her in all matters great and small using the very strongest oaths he knew. And Katara, thinking it only fair, swore that he would have all her blessings with which to face all the perils he should ever come to meet.

Once done with that, the thief pressed the crown into her hands, and he told her that because he was sworn to her, 'Now, Before and Forever more,' that he had found the crown for her and not for himself at all. He declared that a thief's oath was stronger than any king's decision, and he swore that no king would ever make him wear a crown or sit on any throne, no matter what royal decisions might have been made. (Though they both agreed it would probably be best if Katara didn't tell her father, just in case).

So then they parted, each well pleased. The thief now had a princess and a lock of pretty hair, and Katara had a thief's oath and the crown's warm metal firmly in her hands. With it, she marched back into the city, her eyes flashing and her chin held high before all the people who caught their breathes as she stepped up before her father.

The king was overjoyed, and he kissed his daughter upon her forehead and told her quietly that he was *very* pleased, which was something for a man who had never been very much of anything. The people, however, were outraged and they all felt as though they had been greatly wronged in some way, and they complained and griped all the way back to their homes and they swore that this was but the beginning of all the troubles doomed to come.

And they were right.

Four years have passed since that day. . .

OH HO! The nights have flown so fast since your good master swept you off to safety. And four years! Such a long journey for one so young... Horse's backs and salty decks.., I declare! But the guise of traveler suits you well I think..! And I have waited. And see..? Here you are come back to me, and, oh horrors! Here I still am! And I've not been idle... I'm afraid this may hurt a touch my darling little thief... Welcome home.

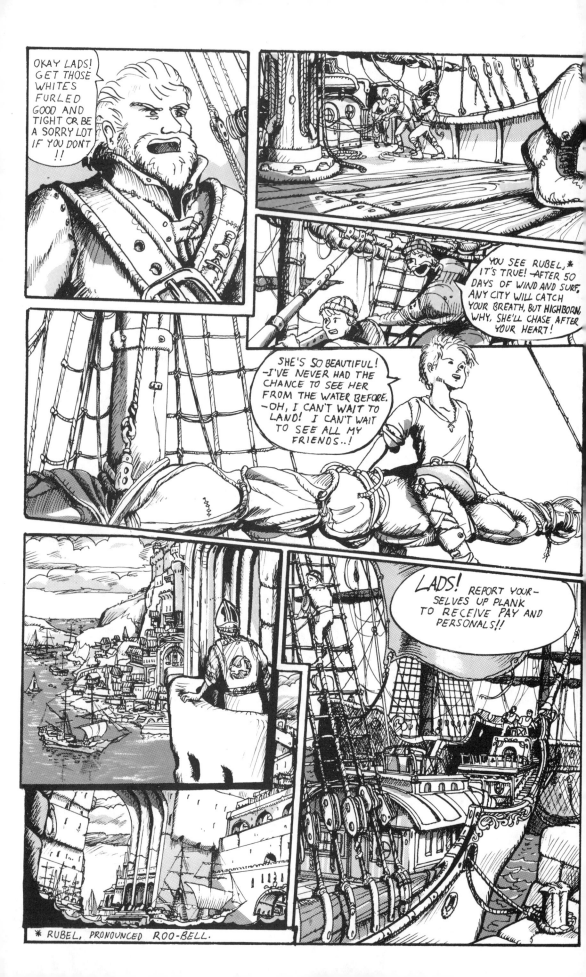

I'M SORRY RUBEL. I HAVEN'T GOT ANYTHING HERE FOR YOU. —CAPTAIN WANTS YOU ON BOARD. —MAYBE NEXT PORT.

WHAT?

BUT THIS IS MY LAST DAY. I'M NOT **GOING** TO NEXT PORT..!

OH YOU AREN'T, ARE YOU? —BETTER SPEAK TO THE CAPTAIN ABOUT IT THEN, BECAUSE I HAVEN'T GOT ANY PAY OR ANY PAPERS WITH YOUR NAME HERE...

KNOCK KNOCK

EXCUSE ME SIR, CAN I COME IN?

WHAT DO YOU WANT BOY?

MY PAY SIR... —WILLY SAYS I'M NOT TO BE PAID UNTIL NEXT PORT, BUT I'M NOT EVEN **GOING** TO NEXT PORT... AND ALSO I NEED MY PAPERS, OR ELSE THEY WON'T LET ME STAY ON SHORE.

YOU'RE NOT GOING ASHORE. YOU ARE NEEDED ON BOARD TO HELP WITH THE CARGO. WE WILL HOLD YOUR PAY UNTIL WE REACH THE SOUTHERN ISLANDS. NOW GET BACK ON DECK.

BUT CAPTAIN! I'M SUPPOSED TO GO ASHORE **HERE**, REMEMBER..? MY GRANDFATHER AND YOU TALKED ABOUT IT. I HAVE TO **MEET** HIM HERE. I'M NOT SUPPOSED TO **GO** TO THE ISLANDS !

YOU ARE **SUPPOSED** TO GO WHERE I TELL YOU BOY. IF YOUR GRANDFATHER, OR ANYONE ELSE WANTS TO BUY YOUR HANDS FROM ME, **THEN** PERHAPS SOMETHING CAN BE ARRANGED, BUT UNTIL THEN, YOU'LL GO NORTH OR SOUTH AND WHEREVER ELSE THIS SHIP SAILS, AND YOU'LL PULL RIGGING UNTIL **I** DECIDE DIFFERENTLY!—DO YOU UNDERSTAND BOY..!?

BUT CAPTAIN...

PERHAPS YOU ARE UNAWARE OF THE NAUTICAL LAWS IN REGARD TO YOUR POSITION.

YOU SIGNED ABOARD UNDER THE DESIGNATION OF 'FREE HAND', WHICH WOULD HAVE ALLOWED FOR YOUR RELEASE AT ANY GIVEN PORT. **HOWEVER**, WHEN MR. CURRY BROKE HIS COLLARBONE, IT BECAME YOUR DUTY TO FILL HIS POSITION AS 'JIBSMAN' UNTIL NEXT PORT **OR** UNTIL THE LEGAL CLOSE OF MR. CURRY'S CONTRACT, PENDING **MY** DECISION.

I HAVE DECIDED THAT DUE TO TIME CONSTRAINTS, MR. CURRY'S CONTRACT WILL **NOT** BE RENDERED VOID. YOU WILL SERVE ABOARD THIS SHIP UNTIL WE DOCK IN STONEGREENWALL THIS COMING SEPTEMBER.

BUT THAT'S CRAZY! IT'S NOT **NECESSARY!** YOU COULD FIND A **HUNDRED** PEOPLE TO SIGN ON AS JIBSMAN RIGHT OFF THE DOCK !!

YOU'RE ONLY KEEPING BECAUSE YOU WANT TO MAKE MY GRANDFATHER **PAY** TO GET ME OFF THIS SHIP..!

YOU'RE NOTHING BUT A **PIRATE!**

MR. MANNOCK, I DON'T THINK OUR YOUNG JIBSMAN CAN BE TRUSTED NOT TO DESERT. PLEASE HAVE HIM LOCKED UP IN THE FORECASTLE UNTIL FURTHER NOTICE. —AND LET THE MEN KNOW THAT SHOULD HE GO MISSING, IT WILL COME OUT OF THEIR WAGES.

AYE CAPTAIN.

!

OH NO YOU DON'T!

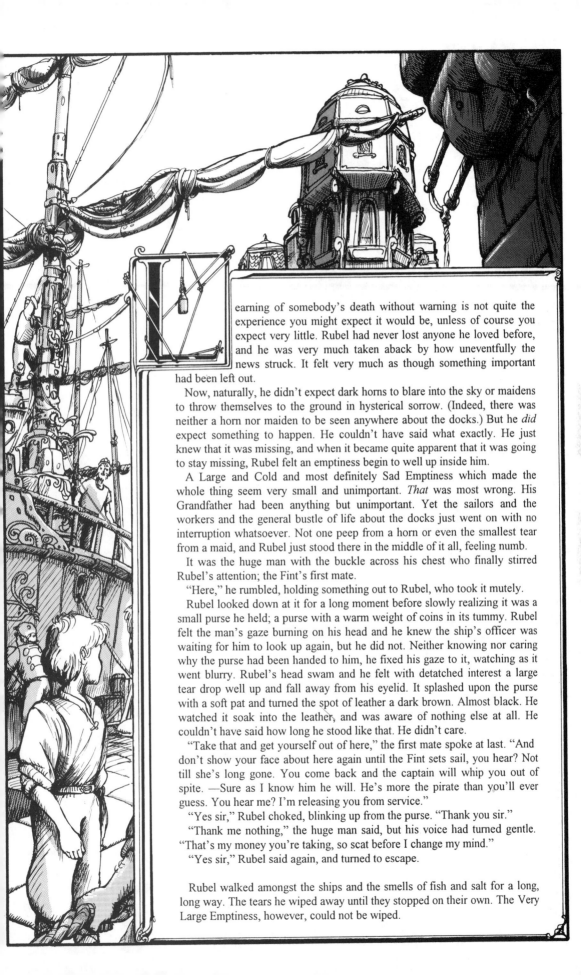

Learning of somebody's death without warning is not quite the experience you might expect it would be, unless of course you expect very little. Rubel had never lost anyone he loved before, and he was very much taken aback by how uneventfully the news struck. It felt very much as though something important had been left out.

Now, naturally, he didn't expect dark horns to blare into the sky or maidens to throw themselves to the ground in hysterical sorrow. (Indeed, there was neither a horn nor maiden to be seen anywhere about the docks.) But he *did* expect something to happen. He couldn't have said what exactly. He just knew that it was missing, and when it became quite apparent that it was going to stay missing, Rubel felt an emptiness begin to well up inside him.

A Large and Cold and most definitely Sad Emptiness which made the whole thing seem very small and unimportant. *That* was most wrong. His Grandfather had been anything but unimportant. Yet the sailors and the workers and the general bustle of life about the docks just went on with no interruption whatsoever. Not one peep from a horn or even the smallest tear from a maid, and Rubel just stood there in the middle of it all, feeling numb.

It was the huge man with the buckle across his chest who finally stirred Rubel's attention; the Fint's first mate.

"Here," he rumbled, holding something out to Rubel, who took it mutely.

Rubel looked down at it for a long moment before slowly realizing it was a small purse he held; a purse with a warm weight of coins in its tummy. Rubel felt the man's gaze burning on his head and he knew the ship's officer was waiting for him to look up again, but he did not. Neither knowing nor caring why the purse had been handed to him, he fixed his gaze to it, watching as it went blurry. Rubel's head swam and he felt with detached interest a large tear drop well up and fall away from his eyelid. It splashed upon the purse with a soft pat and turned the spot of leather a dark brown. Almost black. He watched it soak into the leather, and was aware of nothing else at all. He couldn't have said how long he stood like that. He didn't care.

"Take that and get yourself out of here," the first mate spoke at last. "And don't show your face about here again until the Fint sets sail, you hear? Not till she's long gone. You come back and the captain will whip you out of spite. —Sure as I know him he will. He's more the pirate than you'll ever guess. You hear me? I'm releasing you from service."

"Yes sir," Rubel choked, blinking up from the purse. "Thank you sir."

"Thank me nothing," the huge man said, but his voice had turned gentle. "That's my money you're taking, so scat before I change my mind."

"Yes sir," Rubel said again, and turned to escape.

Rubel walked amongst the ships and the smells of fish and salt for a long, long way. The tears he wiped away until they stopped on their own. The Very Large Emptiness, however, could not be wiped.

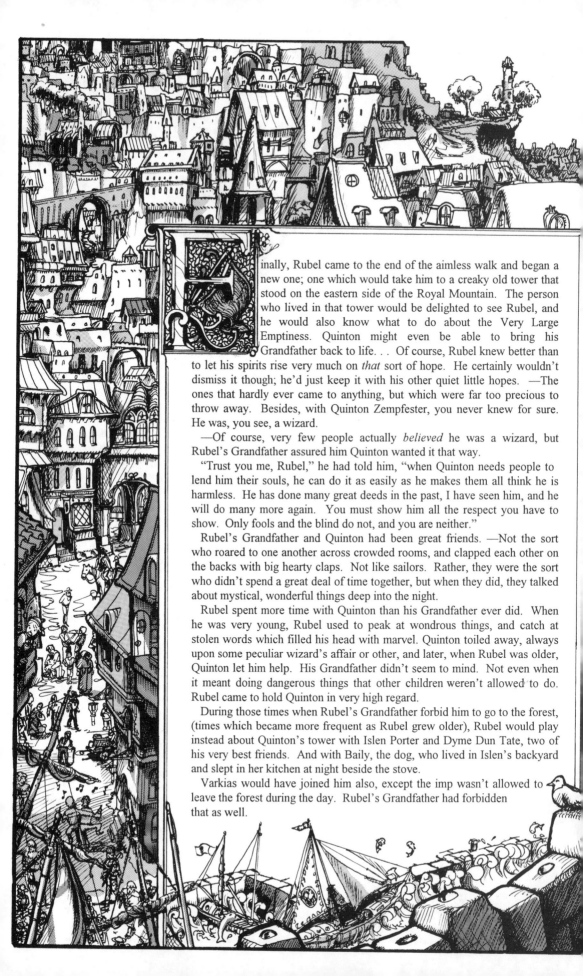

inally, Rubel came to the end of the aimless walk and began a new one; one which would take him to a creaky old tower that stood on the eastern side of the Royal Mountain. The person who lived in that tower would be delighted to see Rubel, and he would also know what to do about the Very Large Emptiness. Quinton might even be able to bring his Grandfather back to life. . . Of course, Rubel knew better than to let his spirits rise very much on *that* sort of hope. He certainly wouldn't dismiss it though; he'd just keep it with his other quiet little hopes. —The ones that hardly ever came to anything, but which were far too precious to throw away. Besides, with Quinton Zempfester, you never knew for sure. He was, you see, a wizard.

—Of course, very few people actually *believed* he was a wizard, but Rubel's Grandfather assured him Quinton wanted it that way.

"Trust you me, Rubel," he had told him, "when Quinton needs people to lend him their souls, he can do it as easily as he makes them all think he is harmless. He has done many great deeds in the past, I have seen him, and he will do many more again. You must show him all the respect you have to show. Only fools and the blind do not, and you are neither."

Rubel's Grandfather and Quinton had been great friends. —Not the sort who roared to one another across crowded rooms, and clapped each other on the backs with big hearty claps. Not like sailors. Rather, they were the sort who didn't spend a great deal of time together, but when they did, they talked about mystical, wonderful things deep into the night.

Rubel spent more time with Quinton than his Grandfather ever did. When he was very young, Rubel used to peak at wondrous things, and catch at stolen words which filled his head with marvel. Quinton toiled away, always upon some peculiar wizard's affair or other, and later, when Rubel was older, Quinton let him help. His Grandfather didn't seem to mind. Not even when it meant doing dangerous things that other children weren't allowed to do. Rubel came to hold Quinton in very high regard.

During those times when Rubel's Grandfather forbid him to go to the forest, (times which became more frequent as Rubel grew older), Rubel would play instead about Quinton's tower with Islen Porter and Dyme Dun Tate, two of his very best friends. And with Baily, the dog, who lived in Islen's backyard and slept in her kitchen at night beside the stove.

Varkias would have joined him also, except the imp wasn't allowed to leave the forest during the day. Rubel's Grandfather had forbidden that as well.

When Rubel was young, he figured that the reason for not allowing little Varkias to the city was so people wouldn't try to catch him and kill him. And though it made Varkias grumpy and irritable, it was a good enough reason for Rubel. Yet even so, he felt there was something more to it than just that. Something important.

He tried to ask Quinton about it, but found it difficult to explain exactly what his question was. Rubel was only eight years old then, and words for eight year olds are not as easy to fit around complicated ideas as they are for older people. He didn't bother with it again. There were more distracting concerns at hand. That day he was helping Quinton build a device which would let them speak with birds.

When it was done, the device worked for Quinton and Islen and even for Dyme Dun, who hardly ever got Quinton's things to work. It even worked for Baily, and he was a dog. In fact, it worked for all of them except Rubel, and he tried the hardest. Islen, (who was feeling mean that afternoon), teased him and stuck out her tongue and they got into a fight which ended with Rubel stomping away saying angry things. He said he hoped the stupid thing broke.

The very next day, they found it shattered on the floor, and they all thought he had done it. Rubel insisted he had seen in the moonlight, a shadow person climb out of the tower window, but he was sure they didn't believe him. —Baily did, and he would have said angrily that Rubel would never lie about such a thing, but all Baily could do was growl.

Quinton believed. And he believed it enough to frown and look troubled by the news. Rubel was eternally grateful to him for that.

But that was all long ago. Now Quinton had vanished as well.

GONE OUT. BUSY. BACK SOON. Q.Z.

No Rubel, not here. Not now. —Once Perhaps, if you'd known the questions.

But you didn't.

And now.

it's far too late.

He's gone.

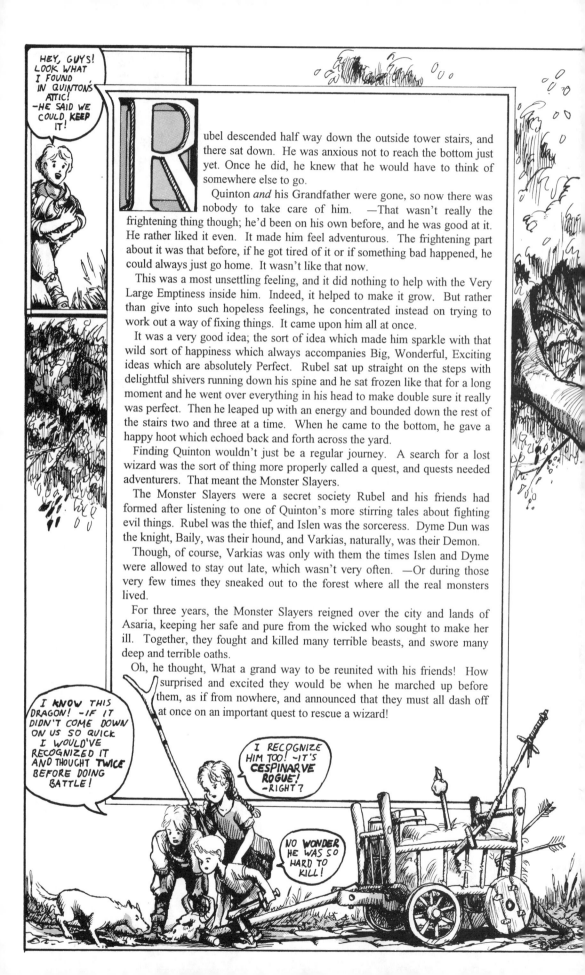

ubel descended half way down the outside tower stairs, and there sat down. He was anxious not to reach the bottom just yet. Once he did, he knew that he would have to think of somewhere else to go.

Quinton *and* his Grandfather were gone, so now there was nobody to take care of him. —That wasn't really the frightening thing though; he'd been on his own before, and he was good at it. He rather liked it even. It made him feel adventurous. The frightening part about it was that before, if he got tired of it or if something bad happened, he could always just go home. It wasn't like that now.

This was a most unsettling feeling, and it did nothing to help with the Very Large Emptiness inside him. Indeed, it helped to make it grow. But rather than give into such hopeless feelings, he concentrated instead on trying to work out a way of fixing things. It came upon him all at once.

It was a very good idea; the sort of idea which made him sparkle with that wild sort of happiness which always accompanies Big, Wonderful, Exciting ideas which are absolutely Perfect. Rubel sat up straight on the steps with delightful shivers running down his spine and he sat frozen like that for a long moment and he went over everything in his head to make double sure it really was perfect. Then he leaped up with an energy and bounded down the rest of the stairs two and three at a time. When he came to the bottom, he gave a happy hoot which echoed back and forth across the yard.

Finding Quinton wouldn't just be a regular journey. A search for a lost wizard was the sort of thing more properly called a quest, and quests needed adventurers. That meant the Monster Slayers.

The Monster Slayers were a secret society Rubel and his friends had formed after listening to one of Quinton's more stirring tales about fighting evil things. Rubel was the thief, and Islen was the sorceress. Dyme Dun was the knight, Baily, was their hound, and Varkias, naturally, was their Demon.

Though, of course, Varkias was only with them the times Islen and Dyme were allowed to stay out late, which wasn't very often. —Or during those very few times they sneaked out to the forest where all the real monsters lived.

For three years, the Monster Slayers reigned over the city and lands of Asaria, keeping her safe and pure from the wicked who sought to make her ill. Together, they fought and killed many terrible beasts, and swore many deep and terrible oaths.

Oh, he thought, What a grand way to be reunited with his friends! How surprised and excited they would be when he marched up before them, as if from nowhere, and announced that they must all dash off at once on an important quest to rescue a wizard!

irst he went to the house where Dyme Dun Tate lived. He stepped right up to the front door and rapped the knocker three solid times. A woman answered who was not Dyme's mother, and she told him that the whole Tate family had moved back to Coscove Gates where Dyme's uncle had started a very successful glasswares business and needed Dyme's father to help him if he would. Dyme's father said it was an exciting idea with good prospects, so he packed up his whole family, sold the house and moved to Coscove Gates. And that was the end of that. Rubel's knight was gone.

Undaunted, Rubel went next to the house where Islen Porter lived and knocked on her door. Islen's mother answered and told him that her daughter had married the baker's boy who she now lived upstairs with, and that they were both out working in the bread store down the street, and did he want to come inside and wait until dinner time when they would be back and could sit together with him? Rubel said No, but was persuaded nonetheless. Mrs. Porter had always rather liked him and was delighted to see him again.

She wanted to know where he had gone in the world, and what had become of his handsome Grandfather and she gave Rubel a cup of tea and a small frosted cake and a seat on the nice sofa chair, all of which he accepted miserably and but as politely as he could. He didn't want to tell her about his Grandfather, or about Quinton, and certainly not about his plan to go on a quest with her daughter. He didn't want to tell her, partly because he felt somehow certain that his Big Wonderful plan would sound both silly and awkward there in Mrs. Porter's stuffy living room, but mostly because he knew that Mrs. Porter would immediately feel sorry for him. She would want to take care of him and give him the small cot in their attic to sleep on, and eggs and bacon every morning for breakfast, and for a variety of reasons the mere thought of this was unbearable to him. The purse of coins Mr. Mannock had given to him was already weighing like so many cakes of poison in his mind.

Proper thieves didn't need sympathy. A proper thief would have gone and spoken strong words with his captain and made him pay his rightful wage. —A proper thief would have struck him down if he had not, but Rubel had done neither of these things. Instead he had cried.

So he didn't tell Mrs. Porter all about the troubles he had inside him, and she didn't hug him to her breast and promise to make everything okay. Instead he asked where his dog was.

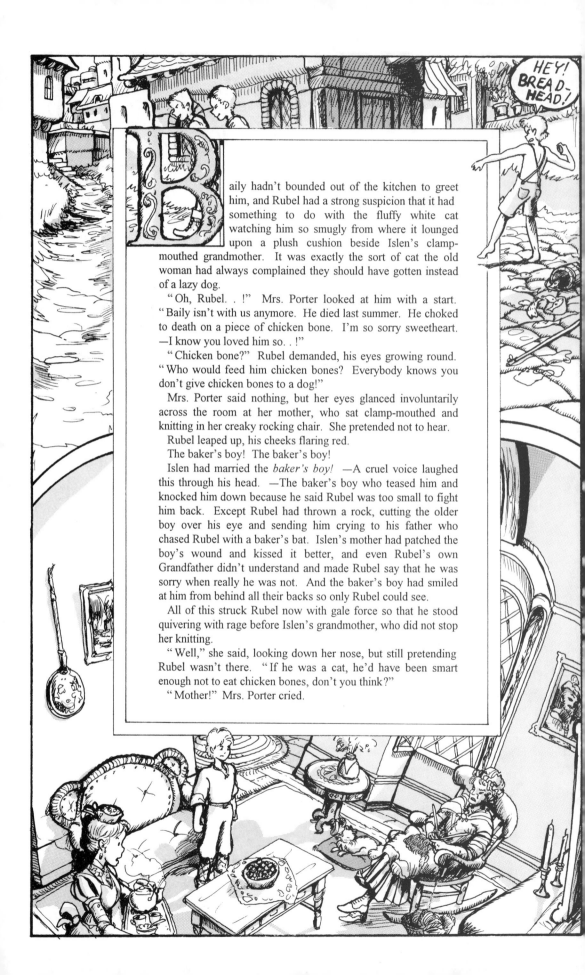

HEY!
BREAD-
HEAD!

aily hadn't bounded out of the kitchen to greet him, and Rubel had a strong suspicion that it had something to do with the fluffy white cat watching him so smugly from where it lounged upon a plush cushion beside Islen's clamp-mouthed grandmother. It was exactly the sort of cat the old woman had always complained they should have gotten instead of a lazy dog.

"Oh, Rubel. . !" Mrs. Porter looked at him with a start. "Baily isn't with us anymore. He died last summer. He choked to death on a piece of chicken bone. I'm so sorry sweetheart. —I know you loved him so. . !"

"Chicken bone?" Rubel demanded, his eyes growing round. "Who would feed him chicken bones? Everybody knows you don't give chicken bones to a dog!"

Mrs. Porter said nothing, but her eyes glanced involuntarily across the room at her mother, who sat clamp-mouthed and knitting in her creaky rocking chair. She pretended not to hear.

Rubel leaped up, his cheeks flaring red.

The baker's boy! The baker's boy!

Islen had married the *baker's boy!* —A cruel voice laughed this through his head. —The baker's boy who teased him and knocked him down because he said Rubel was too small to fight him back. Except Rubel had thrown a rock, cutting the older boy over his eye and sending him crying to his father who chased Rubel with a baker's bat. Islen's mother had patched the boy's wound and kissed it better, and even Rubel's own Grandfather didn't understand and made Rubel say that he was sorry when really he was not. And the baker's boy had smiled at him from behind all their backs so only Rubel could see.

All of this struck Rubel now with gale force so that he stood quivering with rage before Islen's grandmother, who did not stop her knitting.

"Well," she said, looking down her nose, but still pretending Rubel wasn't there. "If he was a cat, he'd have been smart enough not to eat chicken bones, don't you think?"

"Mother!" Mrs. Porter cried.

**R**ubel said nothing but turned and left the house. He tried his best out of respect for Mrs. Porter not to storm and bang the door, but when he was outside everything ran free.

And he sang within his mind. . .

The Angel's Tree!
The Angel's Tree!
I'm going to see the Angel's Tree!

No Knight
No Sorceress, nor Dog have I,

But Varkias, Varkias!
Away up in the Angel's Tree!
Oh let him still be there for me. . !

Rubel sped like wind towards the forest where his very last friend in all the world would be, —his last friend besides Islen, who he was frightened now to see, and besides Mrs. Porter who could not understand magic things.

Mrs. Porter hadn't believed in the wishing key, and she thought Islen had found it and not won it as she had. She took it away from her and gave it to a city guardsmen who she said would know best what to do with it. She told them wisely, "Children shouldn't have things made from gold," and sent them all off home, and her daughter to a bath where she said Islen's ears and knees needed a good scrubbing.

Run then Rubel..!
The forest again!

Varkias! Varkias!
It chanted it through his mind. But something, he felt certain now, was very, very wrong.

T he

Angel's Tree was not the largest tree in the forest, nor was it the most magical, nor even the most beautiful; not to the eye at any rate. But you could crawl into the cup of its palm and there sit entirely apart from all the world and be as content as you could ever be. You could curl up and take a nap, or hum and sing out loud, or think of grand stories where you were the main character, while all about the brooding forest lay. —The Tree was like a desert island in the middle of a dangerous ocean; an island with palm trees and big warm rocks to lie on.

"Oh, Tree, oh Tree," Rubel breathed, "I am back," he said. "I forgot how much I missed you!"

It was true. Just seeing it again made everything seem much better. The Tree had always been there; ever since he could remember. And it could not vanish like Quinton, and it couldn't choke like Baily, nor could it grow up and forget him, or fall into the ocean and drown. The Tree stood as it always had, firmly rooted in the sleeping wood.

"Oh Tree!" Rubel said again, a big warm feeling of relief filling his entire being. "So!" he thought aloud. "I am not alone after all!"

He was wrong though, and when he realized it the warm feeling inside him shuddered and turned at once to ice. It was in the air. —Or rather, it was not.

The Tree's perfume was gone. No warm scent of green and flowered things; of *living* things. Now all he could smell was the leafy decay of the forest floor. —Dead smells, and nothing more.

His heart began to pound very fast and he swung his head up to look into the wreath of branches above. —The wreath of branches which should have been lush with summer foliage. All of them were dry; all bare, but for a scatter of crispy leaves which clung to the ends of kindling stalks and rattled like dead beetle shells. Rubel took a shaky step backwards, a soft lump rising to his throat and the Emptiness yawning wide. The Angel's Tree was dead.

In around clenched teeth Rubel drew a breath, his blood pounding in his ears.

"VARKIAS!" he yelled. He yelled it into the sky, spinning once about in the bright grass with his arms held out at his sides. "VARKIAS!" he cried, "WHERE ARE YOU!"

Nothing.

"VARKIAS!" He called again, his face going red and quivery for how hard he shouted. "IT'S RUBEL! *I'VE COME BACK! I'M BACK FROM THE OCEAN!*"

But the forest swallowed his words entirely, and gave him nothing in reply but the rustle of insects and leaves and the calls of wild birds, —all just mindless chatter above the deep and throaty silence which was the Ancient Wood.

He let his arms sink back to his sides, and he stood with the rawness of his yells sitting in the back of his throat like scraped knees. Then he saw.

Just in the elbow of a branch above him was a little dark shape, with little demon's horns and wings. But something was not quite. . .

Rubel leaped into the tree, both his fear and his hope frozen together by uncertainty. On tip toes he reached into the branch, and there he found the tiny wooden chest he'd hidden once before.

Upon it sat Varkias the imp.

Rubel knew before he touched him that something was dreadfully wrong. Eyes like iron. Wings like iron. Unmoving and cluttered with fallen bits of twig and leaf and old used up spider's web. Just a small iron statue guarding the little box exactly as Rubel had left him.

"Varkias. . !" he breathed.

He had never heard of an imp turning into metal before, but it seemed like the sort of thing an imp might well do. —If something bad happened, perhaps. Like if you left him alone for too long, sitting by himself. . .

This thought stung Rubel so hard his hand seized and Varkias was knocked from his perch. Rubel held himself rigid as the imp tipped from view and a moment later thumped to the crunchy forest floor. Rubel moved to see the statue lying upon its back, gazing up past him with metal eyes, through the dead mesh of branches above, and far into the sky beyond.

A feeling of pure misery burst upon him, like a barrel side smashed in, sloshing out its contents, filling him up so that his head swam and everything in his world turned frothy and bitter. The Emptiness rose up now and this time not to merely chill his heart and weaken him, but to swallow him entirely. He did not try to stop it.

Sometimes when people feel this way, they want to kill themselves. They want to hang themselves or stab themselves, so that the Mrs. Porters in their lives will see them dead and clap their hands to their mouths in horror and utter, "Oh, how horrible!"

And so it was *this* specter the Emptiness chose to release. Rubel remained motionless as it swirled around inside him, laughing and snatching at all the tasty parts from which his mind was made.

Except people didn't just clap their hands to their mouths and say sympathetic things. Rubel knew this. Many people also say secretly within their minds, "Oh, how foolish and useless he must have been to not have had a single friend! How weak he must have been to lie down as such and die! We had no need of him! The very worst of us are better by leaps and bounds, and twice as brave to face our lives and not to wither up like he!"

At this thought, a cloud of flaming anger burst within his head. He pounded a fist upon the tree and yelled out a strangled, wordless cry, startling for a space even the ancient forest from its mammoth brood.

"I *shall* be a thief yet!" he shouted to the sky, "And a *madman* too, if that is what it takes! Let Islen be grown up and married! I don't care a bit! And let them think what they will of me! *I* shall live in the forest! I shall run with animals and I shall be their king! And the people of the land will only see me through the trees, and if they ever bother me, I will bite their necks like a dog! And I will steal a sword and cut off their scalps and wear them on a string around my neck! And the ones I let live will tell all the others until everybody in the land will wonder at me and tell stories about the Wild Thief of the Sleeping Wood!"

Nobody heard though, and nobody cared, so thief or no Rubel sat himself down in the palm of his dead tree and he cried. Properly, for everything he'd lost that day, and for anything else he could think of that was also bitter and sad just to make it feel worse. —Tears to wash the filth away and drown the Emptiness into something small and tired and weak. Except. . .

Before his cheeks got red and puffy with tear water salt. . , before he reached the bottom of his misery and ran out of things to feel sorry for so that he could begin to rise again and feel better; before any of these healthy things could happen, something very different happened to him instead.

T hrough the woods like smoke and shadow she came and into the clearing without a sound. Cloaked from head to toe in all her dark majesty, she rose before Rubel and bid him well the day, saying, "What is this now, my thief?" her words moving like the silk of her hood which she let fall back. She had soft black hair, and eyes like powdered ash, —eyes which twinkled nonetheless, like moonlight on melting ice, all unveiled before him so that he could see. "All in tears I find you," said she. "All in tears, Rubel! Tell me now, what is this?"

She was tall and she was beautiful and she smelled of old autumn leaves. Rubel's breath was taken quite away, and all at once he felt as though he were very small again. He dashed away his remaining tears with the crook of his sleeve and he wanted to stand up and face her like a proper thief ought, but he had been caught in the middle of his weeping and so his thoughts and senses were hopelessly mixed up.

"You are scared of me?" she asked. —She asked it in a curious way, moving forward with such a grace as only supernatural creatures are able.

"I am not scared of anything!" he told her.

"You are a liar."

"I am not! Who are you?"

"You are a liar twice," she said. "You know who I am, but you are afraid to tell me how."

"I am not afraid! I have never seen you before."

"Never?" she asked, raising up one eyebrow. Careful, now Rubel," she said. "Careful now! You have only three chances, and in half a breath you have used up two. If you spend as well the third as such, avoiding petty fears, then that is how you will spend the rest of your days. Your heart will go blind and you will live and die a common man and never know a magic thing again."

"I am here," she said, her eyes shining darkly, "because I am evil. I am rage. I am loneliness and pain. —But I am also love where there is none. And many things as well you don't know that you are, all of which beg forth from your heart for my attention.

"I can breath water," she said, "and so can you so long as you hold my hand. And I will not vanish and I will not let go of you. I would hold you as tightly as you hold me. And I won't grow old, and neither will you, so long as you wish to be a boy and we are friends dear and true. Every thought we ever have the other will think as well. Not a secret would we keep nor would we ever need to; we would understand each other as far as truth can go."

Rubel tried to nod, mesmerized by her eyes.

"Do you want to be mine then?" she asked. "Do you want to take my hand? —Think carefully now, Rubel. Forever is not a thing into which a boy should leap without a care."

Rubel thought.

"If I come," he asked in a quiet breath, "will I be evil too?"

She smiled, gentle, just for him.

"The only evil that there is happens when you are untrue to your nature. —You have heard that said a hundred different ways, a *thousand* different times, but if you manage to believe it only once, the world will be yours forever."

This swirled around Rubel, ringing exotic and elusive in his ears. The Shadow Lady raised her hand and he wanted then, more than anything in the world, to let her lovely fingers close around his own.

It was then that Varkias woke up, and it was very important that he did. He and the tree, (neither of whom were really dead), both knew that the Shadow Lady, while she was neither lying nor forceful in her method, was nonetheless trying to steal Rubel away from them, and they both loved him far too much to want to let him go. Of trees and imps, however, only Varkias could warn him.

he's trying to catch you!" he cried, "Don't let her touch you! Don't let her!"

Rubel's mind was swimming, the dark spell cloaking him now at the deepest swell of its power. But there was just enough still working properly inside his head, *just* enough, to hear the imp and pause before his fingers would have brushed into her palm. And though she might easily have done so, the Queen of Halves did not snatch his hand. A thief's hand might be caught, but never his heart. Not like that. Varkias flapped into the air, and in a flurried instant, stood upon Rubel's shoulder and yelled into his ear.

"Rubel, you mustn't touch her! She's only telling half the truth! She's more than what she says she is! She's something else instead!"

Rubel looked at the imp, his eyes slightly glazed.

"I saw her!" Varkias told him breathlessly. "I saw her the day you were a baby! She came through the trees and her eyes were on fire, and she took the blanket you were wrapped up inside and tried to fly away. And she fought with the Angel and she killed her! She slew her through her middle with a sword black as night! But her wings got cut and your Grandfather had a hammer with a head as big as an anvil, and he swung it back and forth and roared like a giant and frightened her away!"

STAY IN THE TREE RUBEL.

SHE CAN'T TOUCH US IF WE'RE IN THE TREE.

YOU WANT ME TO REASSURE YOU..?

NO. YOU HAVE TO FOLLOW YOUR OWN SOUL. IF YOU DO NOT WANT ME, THEN YOU MUST SEND ME AWAY.

THAT'S RIGHT! SEND HER AWAY!

SHE ONLY WANTS TO STEAL YOUR SOUL!

DID YOU TURN HIM INTO METAL?

SHE DID! -SHE CAST A SPELL ON ME!

TO TRY TO MAKE ME TAKE YOUR HAND?

I TOLD YOU ALREADY.

I AM EVIL.

AND DID YOU ALSO...!

WHAT?

DID SHE ALSO WHAT?

WHAT ELSE HAVE YOU DONE WITCH WOMAN?!

I AM NOT A WITCH.

REMEMBER THAT.

ALL OF WHAT YOU KNOW OF ME IS NOTHING.

INDEED...

—ALL I KNOW OF YOU.

WE LIVE TOGETHER IN A PLACE WHERE ALL TRUTHS SPEAK IN HALVES, RUBEL.

REMEMBER THAT AS WELL.

AND THIS,

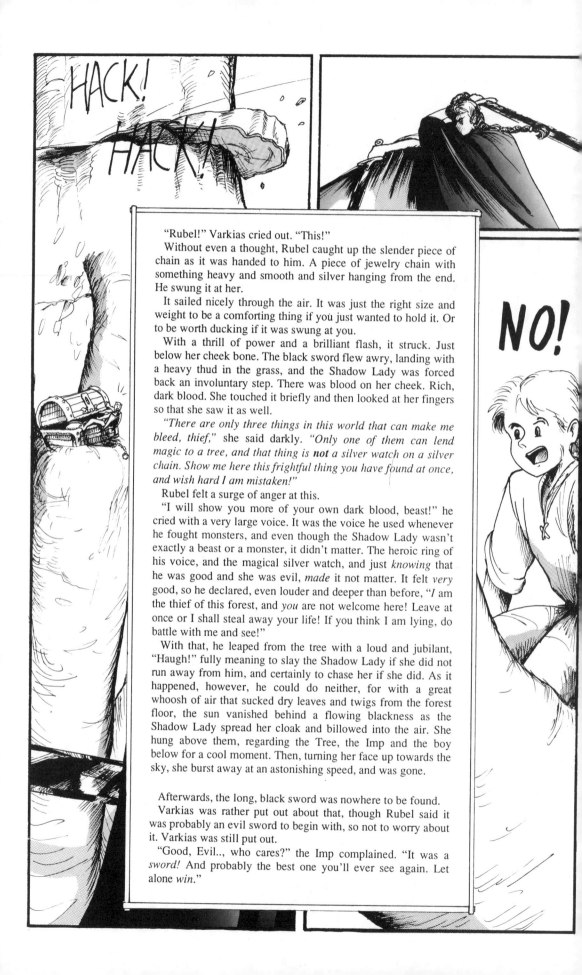

HACK!

HACK!

NO!

"Rubel!" Varkias cried out. "This!"

Without even a thought, Rubel caught up the slender piece of chain as it was handed to him. A piece of jewelry chain with something heavy and smooth and silver hanging from the end. He swung it at her.

It sailed nicely through the air. It was just the right size and weight to be a comforting thing if you just wanted to hold it. Or to be worth ducking if it was swung at you.

With a thrill of power and a brilliant flash, it struck. Just below her cheek bone. The black sword flew awry, landing with a heavy thud in the grass, and the Shadow Lady was forced back an involuntary step. There was blood on her cheek. Rich, dark blood. She touched it briefly and then looked at her fingers so that she saw it as well.

"There are only three things in this world that can make me bleed, thief," she said darkly. *"Only one of them can lend magic to a tree, and that thing is **not** a silver watch on a silver chain. Show me here this frightful thing you have found at once, and wish hard I am mistaken!"*

Rubel felt a surge of anger at this.

"I will show you more of your own dark blood, beast!" he cried with a very large voice. It was the voice he used whenever he fought monsters, and even though the Shadow Lady wasn't exactly a beast or a monster, it didn't matter. The heroic ring of his voice, and the magical silver watch, and just *knowing* that he was good and she was evil, *made* it not matter. It felt *very* good, so he declared, even louder and deeper than before, *"I am the thief of this forest, and you are not welcome here! Leave at once or I shall steal away your life! If you think I am lying, do battle with me and see!"*

With that, he leaped from the tree with a loud and jubilant, "Haugh!" fully meaning to slay the Shadow Lady if she did not run away from him, and certainly to chase her if she did. As it happened, however, he could do neither, for with a great whoosh of air that sucked dry leaves and twigs from the forest floor, the sun vanished behind a flowing blackness as the Shadow Lady spread her cloak and billowed into the air. She hung above them, regarding the Tree, the Imp and the boy below for a cool moment. Then, turning her face up towards the sky, she burst away at an astonishing speed, and was gone.

Afterwards, the long, black sword was nowhere to be found.

Varkias was rather put out about that, though Rubel said it was probably an evil sword to begin with, so not to worry about it. Varkias was still put out.

"Good, Evil.., who cares?" the Imp complained. "It was a *sword!* And probably the best one you'll ever see again. Let alone *win.*"

Chapter 2

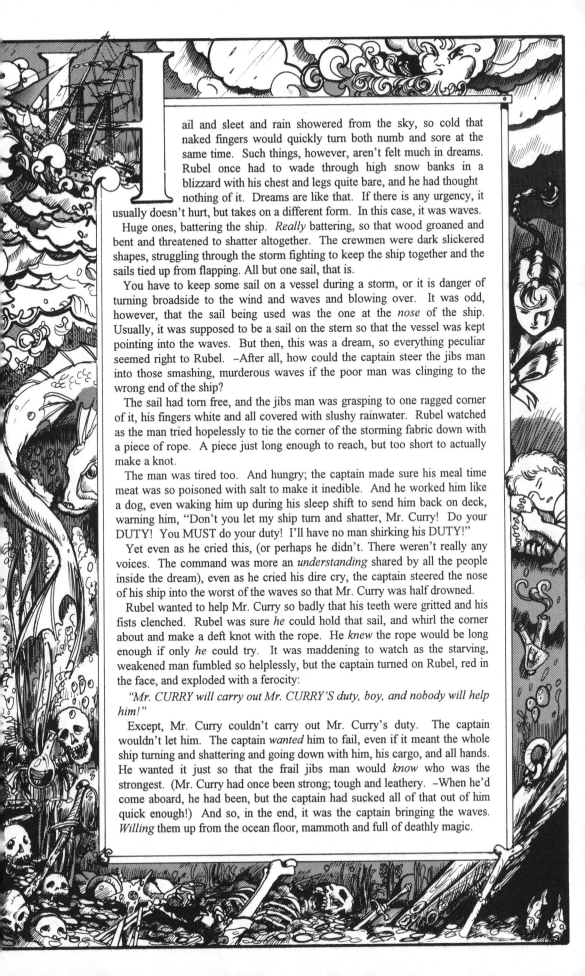

ail and sleet and rain showered from the sky, so cold that naked fingers would quickly turn both numb and sore at the same time. Such things, however, aren't felt much in dreams. Rubel once had to wade through high snow banks in a blizzard with his chest and legs quite bare, and he had thought nothing of it. Dreams are like that. If there is any urgency, it usually doesn't hurt, but takes on a different form. In this case, it was waves.

Huge ones, battering the ship. *Really* battering, so that wood groaned and bent and threatened to shatter altogether. The crewmen were dark slickered shapes, struggling through the storm fighting to keep the ship together and the sails tied up from flapping. All but one sail, that is.

You have to keep some sail on a vessel during a storm, or it is danger of turning broadside to the wind and waves and blowing over. It was odd, however, that the sail being used was the one at the *nose* of the ship. Usually, it was supposed to be a sail on the stern so that the vessel was kept pointing into the waves. But then, this was a dream, so everything peculiar seemed right to Rubel. –After all, how could the captain steer the jibs man into those smashing, murderous waves if the poor man was clinging to the wrong end of the ship?

The sail had torn free, and the jibs man was grasping to one ragged corner of it, his fingers white and all covered with slushy rainwater. Rubel watched as the man tried hopelessly to tie the corner of the storming fabric down with a piece of rope. A piece just long enough to reach, but too short to actually make a knot.

The man was tired too. And hungry; the captain made sure his meal time meat was so poisoned with salt to make it inedible. And he worked him like a dog, even waking him up during his sleep shift to send him back on deck, warning him, "Don't you let my ship turn and shatter, Mr. Curry! Do your DUTY! You MUST do your duty! I'll have no man shirking his DUTY!"

Yet even as he cried this, (or perhaps he didn't. There weren't really any voices. The command was more an *understanding* shared by all the people inside the dream), even as he cried his dire cry, the captain steered the nose of his ship into the worst of the waves so that Mr. Curry was half drowned.

Rubel wanted to help Mr. Curry so badly that his teeth were gritted and his fists clenched. Rubel was sure *he* could hold that sail, and whirl the corner about and make a deft knot with the rope. He *knew* the rope would be long enough if only *he* could try. It was maddening to watch as the starving, weakened man fumbled so helplessly, but the captain turned on Rubel, red in the face, and exploded with a ferocity:

"Mr. CURRY will carry out Mr. CURRY'S duty, boy, and nobody will help him!"

Except, Mr. Curry couldn't carry out Mr. Curry's duty. The captain wouldn't let him. The captain *wanted* him to fail, even if it meant the whole ship turning and shattering and going down with him, his cargo, and all hands. He wanted it just so that the frail jibs man would *know* who was the strongest. (Mr. Curry had once been strong; tough and leathery. –When he'd come aboard, he had been, but the captain had sucked all of that out of him quick enough!) And so, in the end, it was the captain bringing the waves. *Willing* them up from the ocean floor, mammoth and full of deathly magic.

Exhaustion finally closed its grip on Mr. Curry, and his face contorted with the expression people make when they *know* their disaster is an instant away. A stinging blast of sleety wind ripped the sail from the man's grip, taking one of his fingernails with it. He was flung; his arm went through an iron hard square of rope, right up to his shoulder where it twisted awkwardly, and broke with a resounding crack. Rubel gasped, and the night was eclipsed by the captain's roar, more terrible than the storm itself. All the sailors cowered with fear.

All but Rubel. He didn't cower. He *hated* the captain! With a growl, he leaped into the rigging and fought to catch the wild sail. He would *not* let the captain have his dark victory. He would not! But when the captain saw Rubel on his determined mission, he laughed. Rubel ground his teeth, and went on, catching the sail and tying it to the rope with such force that the knot squeezed as dry as a knob of bone. The captain only laughed.

He laughed because he knew something Rubel did not, and though Rubel couldn't remember what exactly it was, he *did* know he'd been made a fool. The captain's hair flew in the rain like a witch's. His eyes bulged. His skin was white and slick with sleet and his mouth somehow seemed too wide. In Rubel's vision, his captain, captain Lewis Tuck McGovern, seemed to transform into a demon. In revulsion and hate, Rubel's anger flared white hot. And now, the Shadow Lady smiled. She gave to him a sword, black and shiny, —as though fresh with oil.

Rubel seized the sword and leaped at the captain, ramming it through his chest. *Now,* the captain stopped laughing. He made a choking cry instead. Thick, horrid fluid belched from the wound and all the sailors cheered as their captain crumpled and died at Rubel's feet. They cheered, crying, 'Hero!', and even the first mate, who Rubel thought was a very great man, nodded at him with approval. . .

Rubel felt himself waking up.

The dream seeped away as dreams do, and he didn't try to stop it. His chest was sweaty and his stomach tight, but slowly he felt himself ease into the real world. He moved beneath the blanket and sighed as the morning sunlight and smell of fresh dew washed away the dream entirely from his mind. He sighed again and then sat up.

Rubel looked about and spied Varkias sitting high above him. The imp's wings and arms were stretched out in a leisurely yawn.

"Good morning, Varkias," Rubel called up to him, really meaning it.

"Yeah, it's not bad," the imp said, looking around at the misty country side with a speculative sort of look. "You were right, I guess. No bandits came and killed you. Didn't rain either."

"I told you this was a good place."

It was a good place, even when it *did* rain. He'd camped there on occasion when he was young, even going so far as to pack a blanket and pillow into a secret hiding spot. After four years they were still intact. Clean and dry, too.

"Yeah," the imp said vaguely. "–We going to the city today?"

"Uh huh." Rubel's stomach made an empty noise. "I'm starving. The last time I ate was yesterday morning on the ship, and that was just salt meat and biscuit. I'm going to get some real food for breakfast. Some bread and jam. And some oranges. And some eggs and bacon!" he added, smacking his lips.

"You going to steal it?" Varkias asked with an interest.

"No. I have money."

"Oh."

"And after, we're going to see the princess."

Varkias stopped. "We are?"

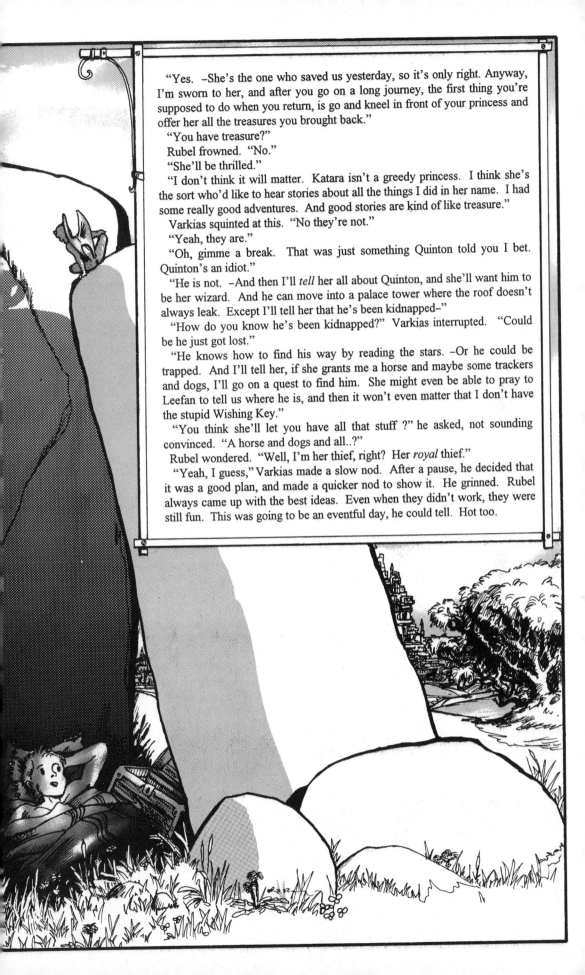

"Yes. –She's the one who saved us yesterday, so it's only right. Anyway, I'm sworn to her, and after you go on a long journey, the first thing you're supposed to do when you return, is go and kneel in front of your princess and offer her all the treasures you brought back."

"You have treasure?"

Rubel frowned. "No."

"She'll be thrilled."

"I don't think it will matter. Katara isn't a greedy princess. I think she's the sort who'd like to hear stories about all the things I did in her name. I had some really good adventures. And good stories are kind of like treasure."

Varkias squinted at this. "No they're not."

"Yeah, they are."

"Oh, gimme a break. That was just something Quinton told you I bet. Quinton's an idiot."

"He is not. –And then I'll *tell* her all about Quinton, and she'll want him to be her wizard. And he can move into a palace tower where the roof doesn't always leak. Except I'll tell her that he's been kidnapped–"

"How do you know he's been kidnapped?" Varkias interrupted. "Could be he just got lost."

"He knows how to find his way by reading the stars. –Or he could be trapped. And I'll tell her, if she grants me a horse and maybe some trackers and dogs, I'll go on a quest to find him. She might even be able to pray to Leefan to tell us where he is, and then it won't even matter that I don't have the stupid Wishing Key."

"You think she'll let you have all that stuff ?" he asked, not sounding convinced. "A horse and dogs and all..?"

Rubel wondered. "Well, I'm her thief, right? Her *royal* thief."

"Yeah, I guess," Varkias made a slow nod. After a pause, he decided that it was a good plan, and made a quicker nod to show it. He grinned. Rubel always came up with the best ideas. Even when they didn't work, they were still fun. This was going to be an eventful day, he could tell. Hot too.

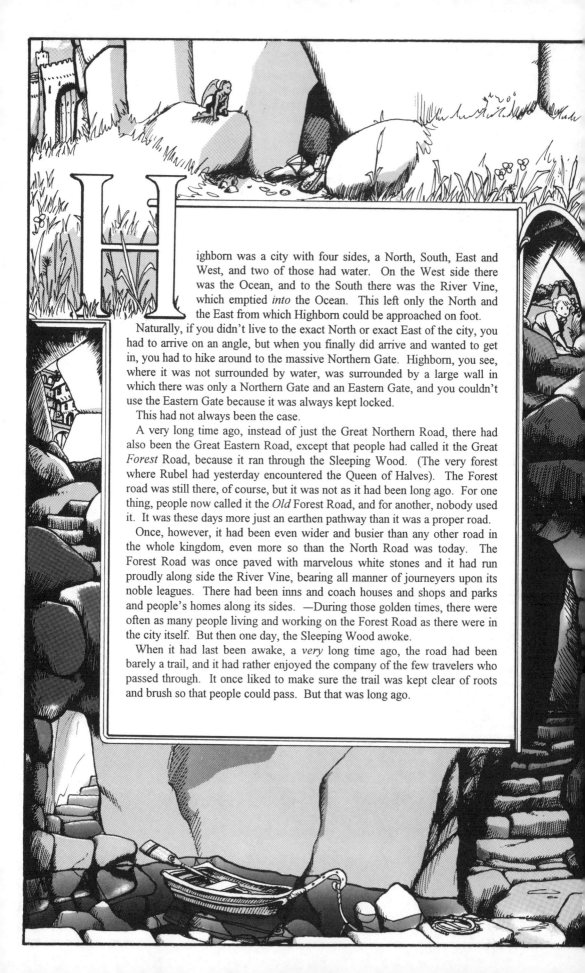

Highborn was a city with four sides, a North, South, East and West, and two of those had water. On the West side there was the Ocean, and to the South there was the River Vine, which emptied *into* the Ocean. This left only the North and the East from which Highborn could be approached on foot.

Naturally, if you didn't live to the exact North or exact East of the city, you had to arrive on an angle, but when you finally did arrive and wanted to get in, you had to hike around to the massive Northern Gate. Highborn, you see, where it was not surrounded by water, was surrounded by a large wall in which there was only a Northern Gate and an Eastern Gate, and you couldn't use the Eastern Gate because it was always kept locked.

This had not always been the case.

A very long time ago, instead of just the Great Northern Road, there had also been the Great Eastern Road, except that people had called it the Great *Forest* Road, because it ran through the Sleeping Wood. (The very forest where Rubel had yesterday encountered the Queen of Halves). The Forest road was still there, of course, but it was not as it had been long ago. For one thing, people now called it the *Old* Forest Road, and for another, nobody used it. It was these days more just an earthen pathway than it was a proper road.

Once, however, it had been even wider and busier than any other road in the whole kingdom, even more so than the North Road was today. The Forest Road was once paved with marvelous white stones and it had run proudly along side the River Vine, bearing all manner of journeyers upon its noble leagues. There had been inns and coach houses and shops and parks and people's homes along its sides. —During those golden times, there were often as many people living and working on the Forest Road as there were in the city itself. But then one day, the Sleeping Wood awoke.

When it had last been awake, a *very* long time ago, the road had been barely a trail, and it had rather enjoyed the company of the few travelers who passed through. It once liked to make sure the trail was kept clear of roots and brush so that people could pass. But that was long ago.

SO...
RUBEL, IF STORIES ARE LIKE TREASURE, THEN HOW COME YOU CAN'T BUY STUFF WITH THEM? —'CAUSE IF THEY WERE, YOU'D BE ABLE TO.

ittle patience did it have for those who would take such rude advantage of it while it slept, what with people cutting down trees they were not supposed to cut, and poking about where they were not supposed to poke. Such practices had a way of dissolving magic into nothing, and magic was the very heart and soul of the Wood.

The Wood's dismay and indignation simmered slowly into an anger which grew deeper and blacker until one day, without any warning at all, the Wood reared up all of its Earth crushing might and struck. The white stones were shattered and the buildings crushed, and the river was choked so that it flooded its banks. Anyone who did not escape was either drowned or swallowed whole. Only the animals got away because they can usually sense when big things like that are about to happen.

This had all been hundreds and hundreds of years ago, but forests don't fall asleep very quickly, and even *now* the Wood was still another century or so away from sinking entirely back into slumber. It still grumbled and shifted and swallowed up travelers every now and then. Even though nearly everyone had forgotten about the flood and the white stones, they were still scared of walking through the forest. The forest only allowed the ones it liked, or knew it must respect, like thieves and shadow queens. Anyone else had to be very careful, or they would be swallowed.

And so, the Eastern Gates were closed and locked. Partly because the forest was wild now and people were worried about wolves and monsters getting in past the city guards. And while this was a sensible enough reason in itself, it was not the only one. The *real* reason was more deeply seated in people's minds; seated far down where thoughts didn't often stray. It had to do with being able to pretend that the forest wasn't really there at all. . .

But the forest *was* there, and so was the road, and for those two things, Rubel was happy. Even after four years of journeying to so many beautiful and terrible lands, he still thought the Sleeping Wood was the most beautiful and terrible of them all. The forest was rather fond of him as well.

WELL, YOU CAN.

YOU CAN TOO.

—IN ALL THE PLACES I'VE STAYED WHERE THERE WERE SAILORS, AND IN INNS AND ROAD HOUSES... ALWAYS THE ONES WHO TOLD THE BEST STORIES, PEOPLE BOUGHT FOOD AND MUGS OF BEER FOR.

YOU CAN NOT.

FOOD? THAT DOESN'T COUNT.

SURE IT DOES.

I WAS SO MAD, I STEPPED RIGHT UP IN FRONT OF HIM AND,

POW!

I PUNCHED HIM RIGHT IN THE NOSE.

HE TRIED NOT TO FALL, BUT HE COULDN'T HELP IT, AND HE LANDED RIGHT ON HIS BACK!

THEN WHAT?

THEN, HE PULLED OUT HIS KNIFE!

REALLY?

YEAH, IT WAS A SHELLY KNIFE, WITH BOTH EDGES SHARP.

WOW. WHAT DID YOU DO?

I KICKED IT OUT OF HIS HAND!

HE WAS STILL ON THE GROUND, AND IT FLEW WAY UP INTO THE AIR OVER ALL THE PEOPLE, AND WHEN IT CAME BACK DOWN, I JUST REACHED OUT AND CAUGHT IT BY THE HILT, JUST AS IF I MEANT TO ALL ALONG.

WOW

YEAH. THEN, I SAID:

PRINCESS KATARA HAS THE MOST PURE HEART THERE EVER WAS! I LOVE HER, AND ANYONE WHO DOES NOT IS EITHER BLIND OR WICKED TO THE CORE!

NOW RUN AWAY, OR I WILL CUT OUT YOUR HEART WITH YOUR OWN KNIFE!

BOY! DID HE RUN?

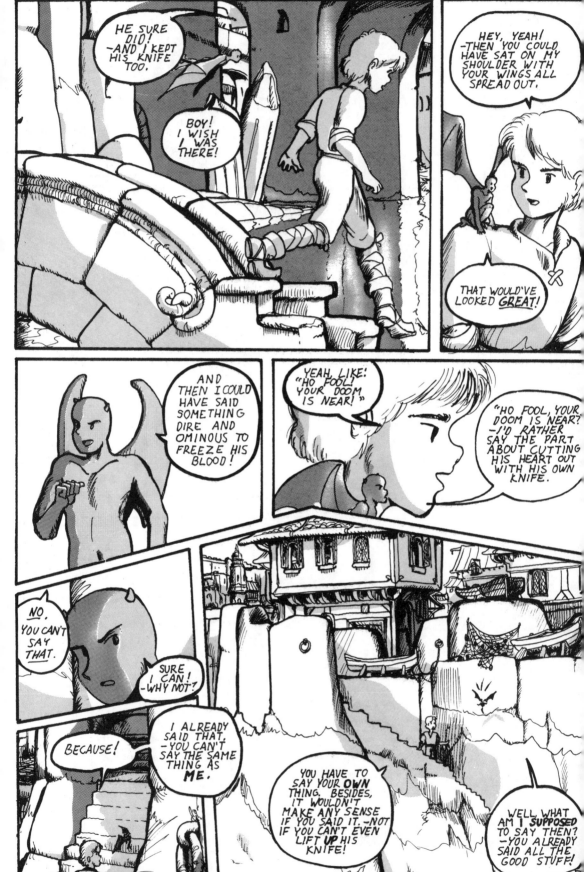

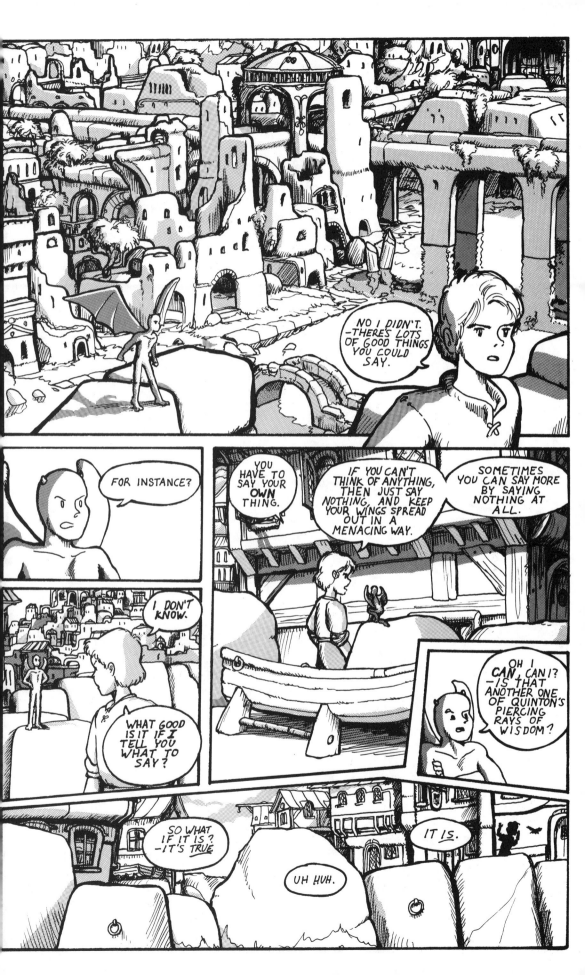

IT WAS SOMETHING ABOUT QUINTON.

WHAT ABOUT HIM?

I DON'T REMEMBER EXACTLY. —IT WAS A LONG TIME AGO.

YOU WERE ONLY THREE.

THREE..?

IT WAS SOMETHING HE SAID... NO, NO..! IT WAS SOMETHING FROM LAST NIGHT!

SOMEBODY WAS THERE!

SOMEBODY WAS WATCHING YOU SLEEP.

VARKIAS, PEOPLE ARE LOOKING AT US..!

RUBEL!

WE SHOULD LEAVE HERE!

WE SHOULD LEAVE HERE RIGHT AWAY!

WE HAVE TO LEAVE BEFORE ..!

MA! LOOK'IT! —ON THAT KID'S SHOULDER! —A LITTLE MAN WITH BAT'S WINGS!

Chapter 3

mps all began out the same way; as human babies, except that before they could be born, their mothers were changed into demons. These babies emerged new into the world not as babies at all, but as fully grown demons. —Fully grown, but in miniature, like tiny men and tiny women. These were the imps.

Hundreds and hundreds of years ago, back in times almost nobody can remember, there were two sorts of demons; the good and the bad. –Nearly as many of one as of the other, but only long ago. Almost all of the good ones were changed back into mortals, and almost all of the bad ones were not.

Varkias' mother was one of the good ones, but she was captured and put into a cave with a big boulder pushed across the opening. She couldn't get out, so she stayed a demon and was never changed back into a woman. Varkias was her son, and she gave birth to him right there in the cave.

She didn't name him Varkias, though.

No sensible mother would don her newborn with a name like 'Varkias', no matter *what* he happened to be. Rather, defiant in the face of Thane, she named him something more suitable for a baby boy. Something like Jeremin or Terry. But deep beneath the burning stone, such defiance was a small and hopeless thing. Still, in a way, this was as she wanted it. —It let her relish the wistful ache which comes with feeling sorry for one's self. For her, this was the only pleasure she would ever know for a long, long time.

She cradled him, and kissed him and she told him that he must slip away; out through a little crack at the foot of the boulder. She told him that he must go find her brothers and tell them to come back for her. Jeremin or Terry nodded solemnly up at his mother and promised to do his very best, and he set off at once to see to it.

The problem, however, is that imps have very short memories. Their heads are so small, when new thoughts come along needing to be remembered, they are more than likely to bump out one or two old thoughts in the process. Such was the case with tiny skulls, or so the wisdom went. Whatever the cause, Varkias forgot all about his mother and all about the promise he had made to her, and soon lost himself in the burning twists and endless crevices beyond.

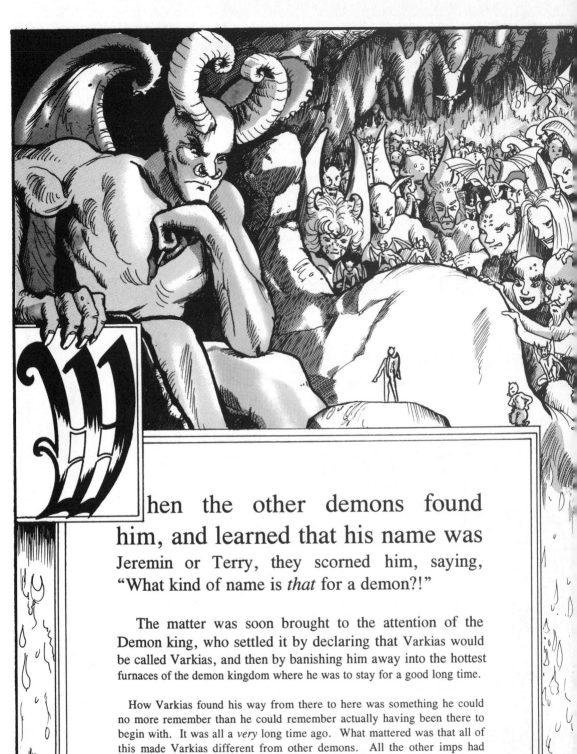

hen the other demons found him, and learned that his name was Jeremin or Terry, they scorned him, saying, "What kind of name is *that* for a demon?!"

The matter was soon brought to the attention of the Demon king, who settled it by declaring that Varkias would be called Varkias, and then by banishing him away into the hottest furnaces of the demon kingdom where he was to stay for a good long time.

How Varkias found his way from there to here was something he could no more remember than he could remember actually having been there to begin with. It was all a *very* long time ago. What mattered was that all of this made Varkias different from other demons. All the other imps had either turned back into babies long ago, or they served still beneath the demon king.

Varkias did neither. For this reason, and for several others, he was a peculiarity in the world of men. But out of all those reasons, there was one of which he was prouder than the rest.

Varkias was a Thief's Companion.

Only Rubel was Rubel. He was not just any thief. (There were hardly any thieves out there as it was. *Real* thieves, that is). Rubel was a *real* thief. And a *princess's* thief no less. Rubel was the sort who'd fought and won against monsters. Monsters, like Chead and the Shadow Lady. Rubel was the sort of thief who punched greasy Geropian bullies flat on their backs with single smashes to their noses. —And stole their knives afterwards for good measure. Varkias was *his* imp.

The problem was that people knew all about *demons.*

Not necessarily all the correct things. Not even things they entirely believed in. Still, being what they are, preconceptions are always the first things people have in their heads when it comes to meeting up with new people and new things.

And so, people knew all about *demons.*

Even tiny ones like him. *Especially* tiny ones like him. Imps meant trouble.

It was said that an imp could make you sick by spitting up your nose, or give you a wart just by poking you. They could blind you by kicking you in the eye, even with your eyelid shut. And if you left your window open at night, an imp might come in and steal your teeth right from your gums while you slept! Everyone who had ever heard a nursery rhyme knew about imps! Imps were nearly as bad as fairies! Except that fairies could also be nice if they wanted to, whereas imps were bad through and through!

The fact of the matter, however, was that most people had never actually *seen* an imp. Never a *real* one. It is difficult to believe in magic things, no matter how much you might like to, when the only kind of magic you've ever known is the sort that a friend once heard about happening to somebody. —Or the laborious, mechanical kind of magic performed with cards and balls and metal rings; that sort looks nice but doesn't really fool anybody.

Thus, the fascination with seeing an actual, live imp; one with bat's wings and tiny horns and everything, easily out-matched everybody's fear of warts and stolen teeth. Particularly in such a sunny, friendly setting as Tamard street.

nd so, Rubel and Varkias found themselves the sudden center of attention. And for Rubel, this meant trouble. It was well known that people got pulled off and tied to wooden posts and set on fire for being friendly with demons. It happened to witches and the sort. Not very often, mind you, but then people didn't often wander into town with imps standing on their shoulders.

Funny part about it was that Rubel *understood* this.

If you were friends with a demon, then quite simply, you didn't parade through town with him. Rubel's Grandfather had told him this. *Quinton*, even, had warned him, and Quinton rarely got very serious about anything. Yet, there he was, and not so much as a nagging doubt had crossed his mind.

That was the main problem, and it struck him as something *profoundly* odd. But he could only wonder at his foolishness for an instant before the consequences merrily began to leap into the forefront of his attention.

"Is he *real?*" somebody breathed, gazing at Varkias in awe.

Varkias turned his head and looked back at the astonished speaker, squinting at him with such fluid facial movements as only a real live creature could perform. The man clapped a hand to his mouth and took a step back.

"Goodness!"

Rubel was vaguely aware that he would probably be best to run away as quickly as he could; back into the alley from which he had come. He didn't, though. The several things all clamoring to be on top of his mind were jumbled up in a strange sort of order. —Indeed, the thought of being burned alive hardly registered at all. Executions and the like seemed distant and unrelated to the here and now of Tamard street.

ow at the very top of all his jumbled thoughts, was the grumble in his stomach. For some reason, his hunger was the thing making most sense. He'd come here with honest money to spend; nearly a whole fistful of silver and brass. He'd come to buy himself some well deserved breakfast, and he had done nothing bad to anybody. Running away would only leave him panting and guilty and most of all, still hungry.

So instead, Rubel looked them all back with his most authoritative look, and he told them all quite firmly, "Yes. He's real."

The crowd made a sound of wonder. They had been waiting on his answer.

Varkias snorted.

"Goodness," said the man again.

"Where did you find him?" asked the boy who had first cried everybody's attention upon the imp and thief.

"In the forest," Rubel told him.

The boy's eyes to opened wider.

"In the Sleeping Wood," Rubel put in for good measure.

"The *Sleeping wood?*" the boy chimed. "Wow!"

"He's not evil," Rubel added.

"He's *good?*"

Varkias snorted again, this time with contempt. The audience reacted with uncertainty.

"Can he *talk?*" the boy asked. "How come you have him? Can he *fly?*"

Everybody looked to Rubel.

ubel felt an impatient movement
on his shoulder.

"What do you mean, can I *talk?*
Of course I can *talk*," Varkias answered the
boy loudly enough for all to hear.   He
sounded not quite irritable, but close to it.
(Varkias hadn't yet decided on what his mood
ought to be for such an occasion as this.
Probably irritable.   Irritable generally served).

The audience made more sounds of wonder
when they heard his voice.

"Wow!" the boy wowed.   "How come you
have him?   Are there more in the forest?   How
did you *get* him?"

Rubel frowned and felt a flurry of powerful
anger burst somewhere inside him.   —Easily
mastered and only very brief, though he could
only guess from where it had come.

"*Get* him?" he asked.   "You don't go and
get friends.   I've known him ever since I was
born."

"Ever since you were *born*?" the
boy repeated, his eyes now flashing like
a pair of green flames.   "You were born
in the *forest.. ?* Are you a *thief?*"

Quick as lightning, that.   Even Rubel
should have been taken aback, except he
wasn't.   The inside of his head had gone a
little fuzzy again.   Not so that he felt confused.
Just a little light.   Everybody leaned in, quiet
enough to give that block of sunny Tamard an
unreal air.   Rubel returned their looks solidly.
His stomach grumbled.

"Yes," he said.   "I am a thief."

A buzz swept through the market, half in
whispers.

"But if you call the guardsmen and the
jailers," he told them loudly, "I'll be gone as
fast as wind, and they won't see even a hair on
my head!"

From the expression people gave, anybody
could tell that not one of them would have
dreamed of calling guardsmen or jailers.
What, with the air smelling so fresh and new
amidst the bright market about them, and the
shining boy and his magic imp before them.

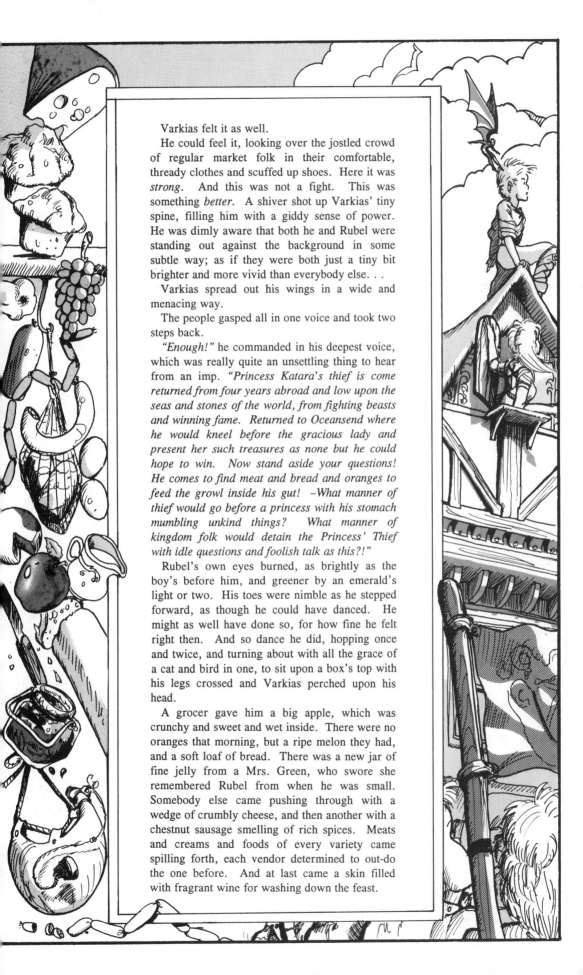

Varkias felt it as well.

He could feel it, looking over the jostled crowd of regular market folk in their comfortable, thready clothes and scuffed up shoes. Here it was *strong*. And this was not a fight. This was something *better*. A shiver shot up Varkias' tiny spine, filling him with a giddy sense of power. He was dimly aware that both he and Rubel were standing out against the background in some subtle way; as if they were both just a tiny bit brighter and more vivid than everybody else. . .

Varkias spread out his wings in a wide and menacing way.

The people gasped all in one voice and took two steps back.

"Enough!" he commanded in his deepest voice, which was really quite an unsettling thing to hear from an imp. *"Princess Katara's thief is come returned from four years abroad and low upon the seas and stones of the world, from fighting beasts and winning fame. Returned to Oceansend where he would kneel before the gracious lady and present her such treasures as none but he could hope to win. Now stand aside your questions! He comes to find meat and bread and oranges to feed the growl inside his gut! –What manner of thief would go before a princess with his stomach mumbling unkind things? What manner of kingdom folk would detain the Princess' Thief with idle questions and foolish talk as this?!"*

Rubel's own eyes burned, as brightly as the boy's before him, and greener by an emerald's light or two. His toes were nimble as he stepped forward, as though he could have danced. He might as well have done so, for how fine he felt right then. And so dance he did, hopping once and twice, and turning about with all the grace of a cat and bird in one, to sit upon a box's top with his legs crossed and Varkias perched upon his head.

A grocer gave him a big apple, which was crunchy and sweet and wet inside. There were no oranges that morning, but a ripe melon they had, and a soft loaf of bread. There was a new jar of fine jelly from a Mrs. Green, who swore she remembered Rubel from when he was small. Somebody else came pushing through with a wedge of crumbly cheese, and then another with a chestnut sausage smelling of rich spices. Meats and creams and foods of every variety came spilling forth, each vendor determined to out-do the one before. And at last came a skin filled with fragrant wine for washing down the feast.

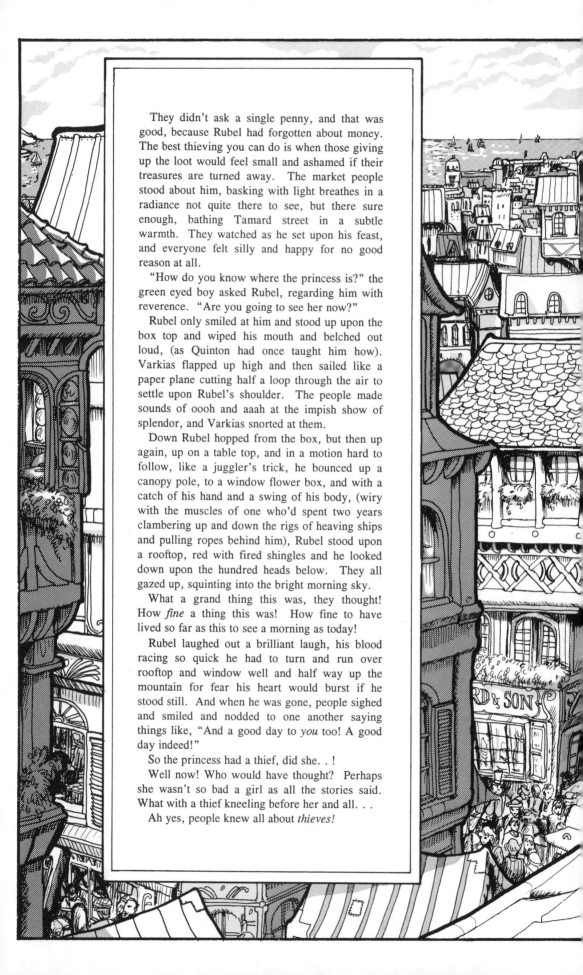

They didn't ask a single penny, and that was good, because Rubel had forgotten about money. The best thieving you can do is when those giving up the loot would feel small and ashamed if their treasures are turned away. The market people stood about him, basking with light breathes in a radiance not quite there to see, but there sure enough, bathing Tamard street in a subtle warmth. They watched as he set upon his feast, and everyone felt silly and happy for no good reason at all.

"How do you know where the princess is?" the green eyed boy asked Rubel, regarding him with reverence. "Are you going to see her now?"

Rubel only smiled at him and stood up upon the box top and wiped his mouth and belched out loud, (as Quinton had once taught him how). Varkias flapped up high and then sailed like a paper plane cutting half a loop through the air to settle upon Rubel's shoulder. The people made sounds of oooh and aaah at the impish show of splendor, and Varkias snorted at them.

Down Rubel hopped from the box, but then up again, up on a table top, and in a motion hard to follow, like a juggler's trick, he bounced up a canopy pole, to a window flower box, and with a catch of his hand and a swing of his body, (wiry with the muscles of one who'd spent two years clambering up and down the rigs of heaving ships and pulling ropes behind him), Rubel stood upon a rooftop, red with fired shingles and he looked down upon the hundred heads below. They all gazed up, squinting into the bright morning sky.

What a grand thing this was, they thought! How *fine* a thing this was! How fine to have lived so far as this to see a morning as today!

Rubel laughed out a brilliant laugh, his blood racing so quick he had to turn and run over rooftop and window well and half way up the mountain for fear his heart would burst if he stood still. And when he was gone, people sighed and smiled and nodded to one another saying things like, "And a good day to *you* too! A good day indeed!"

So the princess had a thief, did she. . !

Well now! Who would have thought? Perhaps she wasn't so bad a girl as all the stories said. What with a thief kneeling before her and all. . .

Ah yes, people knew all about *thieves!*

YOU'RE GOING TO HAVE TO STAY HERE VARKIAS.

HUH?

WHAT ARE YOU TALKING ABOUT?

I HAVE TO DO THIS PART ON MY OWN. -YOU WAIT HERE.

WAIT HERE? WHY DO YOU HAVE TO DO THIS PART ON YOUR OWN?

I'M NOT STAYING UP HERE!

VARKIAS. JUST WAIT HERE. I'LL BE RIGHT BACK.

WHY? WHY SHOULD I? -WHAT IF YOU GET INTO TROUBLE?

IT DOESN'T MATTER EVEN IF I DO. -YOU JUST CAN'T INTERFERE OKAY?

STUPID IDIOT!

YOU JUST WANT TO DO ALL THE GOOD STUFF BY YOURSELF!

I HOPE YOU **DO**, GET STABBED!

OR **SHOT!**

THAT'D SHOW YOU!

THEN **I'D** GET TO DO ALL THE GOOD STUFF ALL BY MY SELF!

ALL ALONE!

AND NOBODY ELSE WOULD BE THERE!

⸓ SIGH ⸓

YEAH. THAT'D BE A PILE OF FUN.

STUPID IDIOT RUBEL!

NOTHING BETTER HAPPEN!

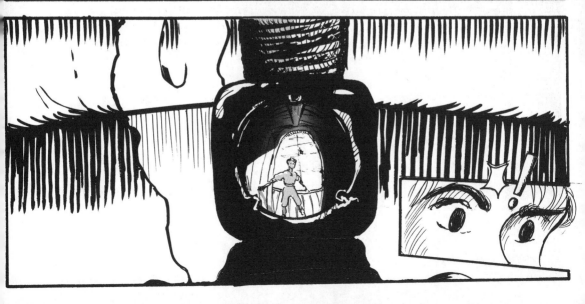

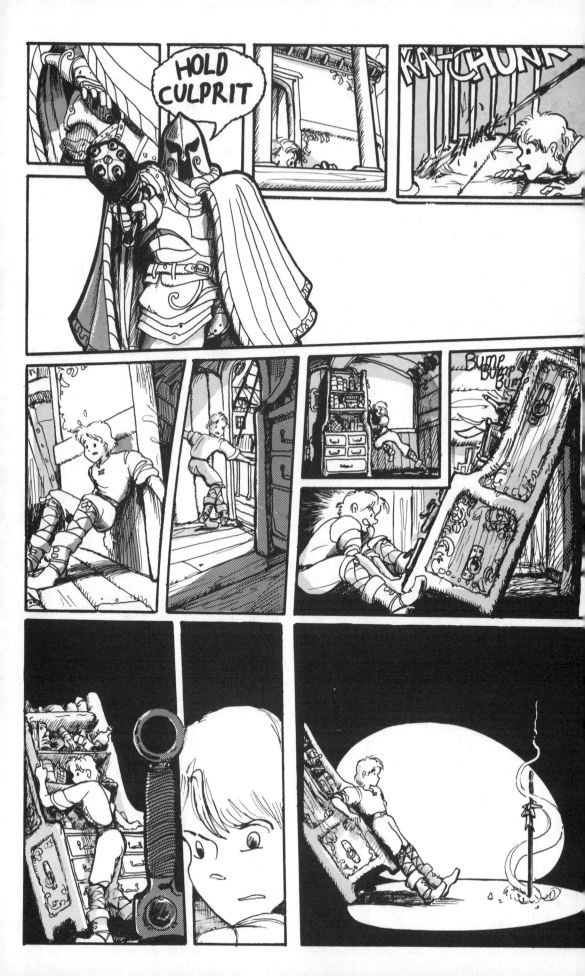

Chapter 4

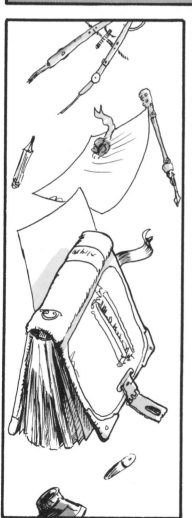

AM! BAM! went the door. Assorted objects rattled and fell around Rubel's ears as he struggled to hold fast his impromptu fortification. With heels jammed into the floor boards and his back pressed into knobbles of wood, book and bolt, he braced the shuddering barricade.

BAM! BAM! BAM!

And the black sword stood silent before him. It gazed at him darkly through a veil of magic that smelled of old and wet autumn leaves, and the black ribbon bow tied about its hilt moved gently in some invisible breeze. Rubel knew who the sword belonged to, and he had a fairly good idea as to why it was there. He was also certain beyond any shadow of a doubt that touching it would be an *astonishingly* bad idea.

BAM! BAM! *SPLINTER!*

Rubel bit his lip and pushed an anxious hand through his hair. What *was* he going to do?

The sword seemed aware of his dilemma, and it throbbed with an unwholesome sort of glee. "Yes, little boy, take hold of me!" it seemed to laugh. "Slide your fingers around my hilt and I shall be your *Sword!* —And you shall be my Boy! If you do not, they'll have your head! I know it! And *you* do as well, I think, but only *I* know why!"

It could cut through metal, Rubel thought with a start. Through *armor*. It would cut their armor as though slicing sheets of wet clay. She would not have placed it there if it could not. Rubel felt the truth of this sink right down to the pit of his stomach. So, he thought, she *is* trustworthy. . , after her own frightful manner.

And who were *they?* He'd never seen before such guardsmen as those now beating outside the door. —Encased in blackened metal from brow to toe; old metal too. *Old.* The sense of age clung about them as it did with family silverware; like the *good* forks people save for occasions.

ubel narrowed his eyes. Occasions. —When the collars were tight and starched and itchy around his neck when he was only five. When shiny shoes boxed his wiggly toes, and when old people came to sit and eat and speak dry and sleepy things; who smelled of liquor and perfume, frightening him in some gentle way that was hard to think of and made him stare. All ancient creatures from some forgotten time. . .

In smoke and war. . .

He blinked and without warning, a memory, musty and strong with age heaved up before him and shook itself. He *had* seen them before. In *pictures*. With dark helmets and crimson capes. —In pictures of *wars*. Quinton had shown him so when he was little.

He shivered and then caught his breath as another realization flashed through his mind. . . A realization from the present.

They were carrying swords.

Enormous swords. Swords which could well be used to. . .

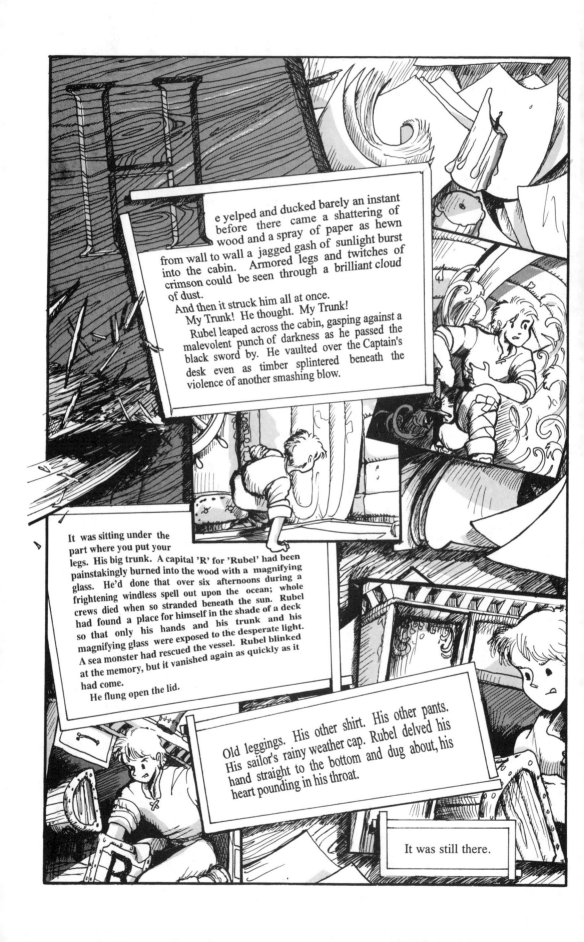

e yelped and ducked barely an instant before there came a shattering of wood and a spray of paper as hewn from wall to wall a jagged gash of sunlight burst into the cabin. Armored legs and twitches of crimson could be seen through a brilliant cloud of dust.

And then it struck him all at once.

My Trunk! He thought. My Trunk!

Rubel leaped across the cabin, gasping against a malevolent punch of darkness as he passed the black sword by. He vaulted over the Captain's desk even as timber splintered beneath the violence of another smashing blow.

It was sitting under the part where you put your legs. His big trunk. A capital 'R' for 'Rubel' had been painstakingly burned into the wood with a magnifying glass. He'd done that over six afternoons during a frightening windless spell out upon the ocean; whole crews died when so stranded beneath the sun. Rubel had found a place for himself in the shade of a deck so that only his hands and his trunk and his magnifying glass were exposed to the desperate light. A sea monster had rescued the vessel. Rubel blinked at the memory, but it vanished again as quickly as it had come.

He flung open the lid.

Old leggings. His other shirt. His other pants. His sailor's rainy weather cap. Rubel delved his hand straight to the bottom and dug about, his heart pounding in his throat.

It was still there.

ubel pulled forth the Geropian shelly knife he had initially come here to get, and he clasped it tight to himself. Its blade gleamed. He'd soaked it in soap. He'd soaked it in oil. He'd polished it hard, poking corners of rag into every crack and crevice until he'd obliterated all trace of Geropian grime until it shone in his hands like a silver flame! All the other sailors who looked had made noises of admiration. It was a fine looking prize, they told him roundly. *Fine* looking!

Rubel stood up, startled for an instant to see that the dark sword had vanished. There was nothing left but the flutter of the black ribbon bow in its place upon the floor. In another instant this too was lost as the door and wall and barricade and all came crashing down beneath a third and final blow.

And there, towering high in the sunlight, crimson and black in velvet capes, stood twin the behemoth warriors. They fixed him with their iron glares, and advanced.

One bore a curving great sword nearly as long as Rubel was tall. The other wielded a five barrel bolt-lock gun so heavy that none but the mightiest of men could have lifted it above his head or, indeed, have have pulled back any of the dread steel coiled in its throat. Deliberately, mechanically, this mighty weapon was raised on Rubel and, with a huge metallic crash, fired.

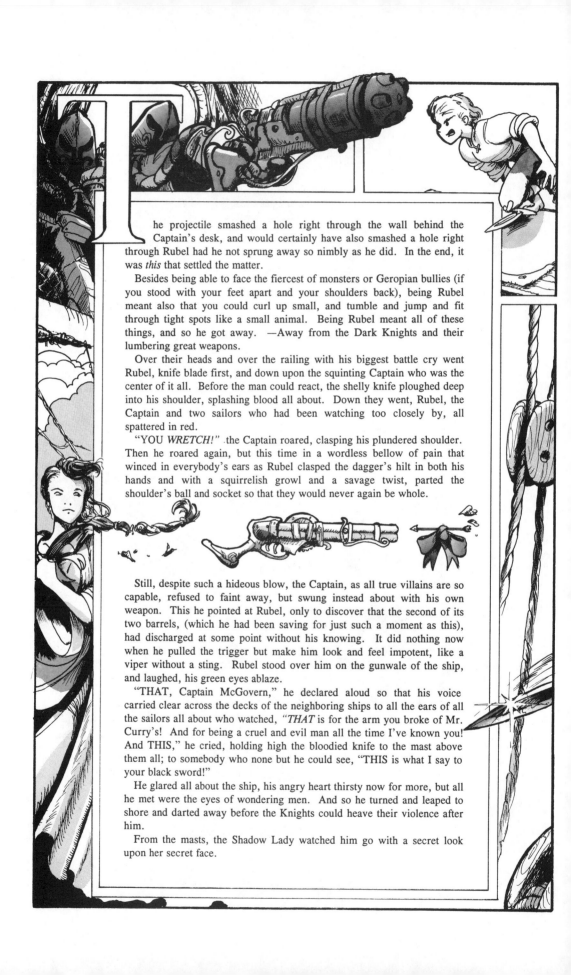

The projectile smashed a hole right through the wall behind the Captain's desk, and would certainly have also smashed a hole right through Rubel had he not sprung away so nimbly as he did. In the end, it was *this* that settled the matter.

Besides being able to face the fiercest of monsters or Geropian bullies (if you stood with your feet apart and your shoulders back), being Rubel meant also that you could curl up small, and tumble and jump and fit through tight spots like a small animal. Being Rubel meant all of these things, and so he got away. —Away from the Dark Knights and their lumbering great weapons.

Over their heads and over the railing with his biggest battle cry went Rubel, knife blade first, and down upon the squinting Captain who was the center of it all. Before the man could react, the shelly knife ploughed deep into his shoulder, splashing blood all about. Down they went, Rubel, the Captain and two sailors who had been watching too closely by, all spattered in red.

"YOU *WRETCH!*" the Captain roared, clasping his plundered shoulder. Then he roared again, but this time in a wordless bellow of pain that winced in everybody's ears as Rubel clasped the dagger's hilt in both his hands and with a squirrelish growl and a savage twist, parted the shoulder's ball and socket so that they would never again be whole.

Still, despite such a hideous blow, the Captain, as all true villains are so capable, refused to faint away, but swung instead about with his own weapon. This he pointed at Rubel, only to discover that the second of its two barrels, (which he had been saving for just such a moment as this), had discharged at some point without his knowing. It did nothing now when he pulled the trigger but make him look and feel impotent, like a viper without a sting. Rubel stood over him on the gunwale of the ship, and laughed, his green eyes ablaze.

"THAT, Captain McGovern," he declared aloud so that his voice carried clear across the decks of the neighboring ships to all the ears of all the sailors all about who watched, *"THAT* is for the arm you broke of Mr. Curry's! And for being a cruel and evil man all the time I've known you! And THIS," he cried, holding high the bloodied knife to the mast above them all; to somebody who none but he could see, "THIS is what I say to your black sword!"

He glared all about the ship, his angry heart thirsty now for more, but all he met were the eyes of wondering men. And so he turned and leaped to shore and darted away before the Knights could heave their violence after him.

From the masts, the Shadow Lady watched him go with a secret look upon her secret face.

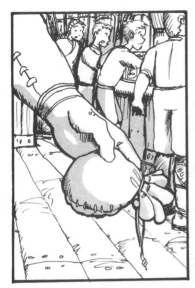

AYE LAD.

POINT MADE.

POINT MADE.

WILL SOMEBODY PLEASE SHOOT THAT WRETCH?!

RUBEL! WHERE ARE WE GOING? SHOULD I HIDE?

NAH. DON'T BOTHER.

HERE. HOLD THIS.

WE'RE GOING TO SEE THE PRINCESS!

SO IT DOESN'T MATTER IF PEOPLE SEE YOU. —SHE'LL TELL EVERY-BODY THAT IT'S OKAY FOR YOU TO BE IN THE CITY. —SHE'LL GRANT YOU ROYAL PERMISSION

YEAH, I GUESS SHE CAN DO THAT, CAN'T SHE.

SURE SHE CAN!

THERE!

HEY YOU!

RUN RUBEL!

RIGHT...

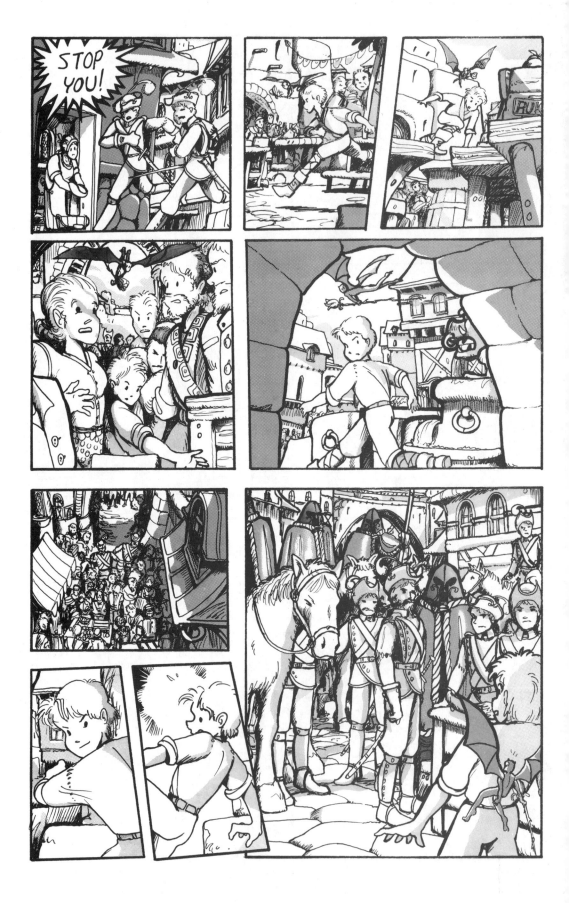

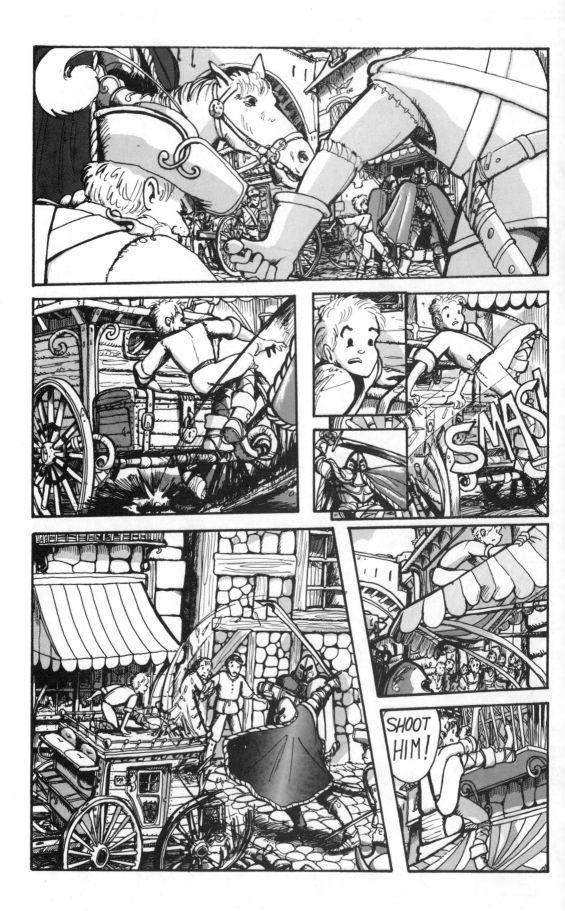

BAM! BAM!
!

OPEN UP! OPEN UP IN THE NAME OF THE PRINCE!

THERE HE GOES!

YES, YES, HURRY!

THE MISSES' HUSBAND IS WITH THE GUARD!

GO UPSTAIRS QUICK! YOU'VE GOT HIM TRAPPED!

SMASH!

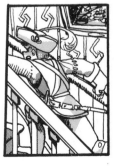

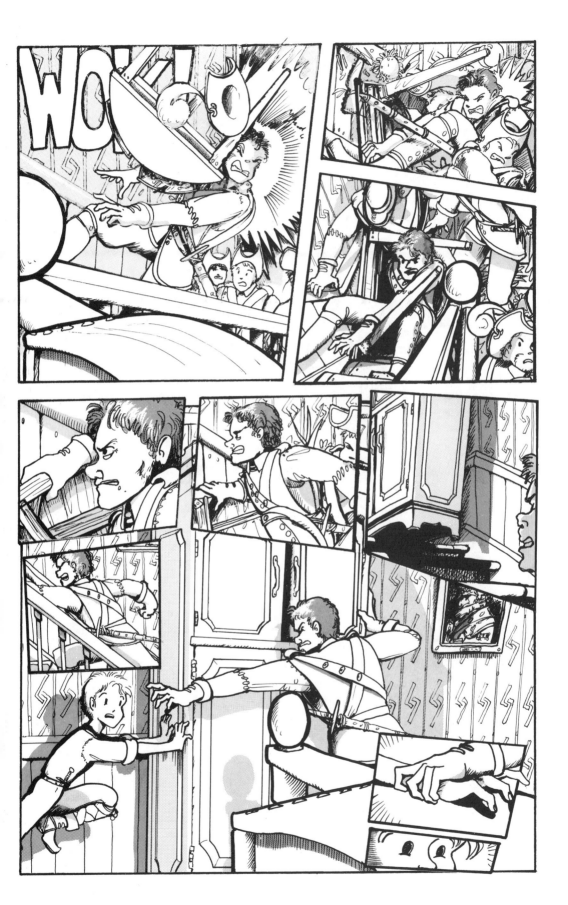

Chapter 5

SHICK!

TINK

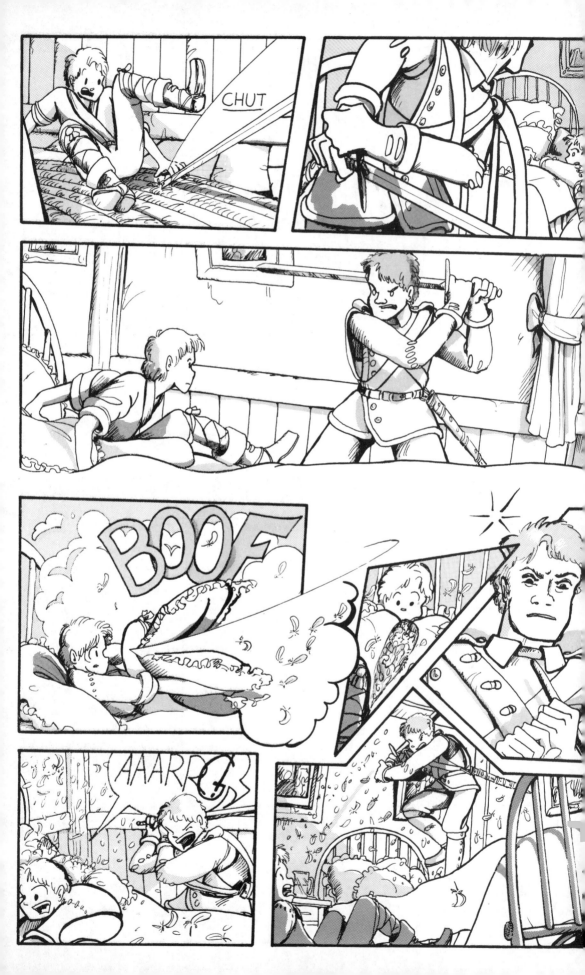

Throwing his weight against the wall, Rubel pushed mightily with both feet on the bed frame. The bed slid back and the guardsman fell forward, dropping his sword in order to catch himself from smashing headlong into the floor, which he did anyway.

Rubel darted for the door.

Just as he reached it, in tumbled all the other guardsmen, all looking sore and mean. Rubel yelped and reversed his direction. With swords drawn and faces red, the guardsmen leaped after him.

Around and around the tiny room they all went, knocking things over and treading on the bed with their dusty boots, and stirring up the air so that it was difficult to breathe without inhaling feathers. Yet, try as they might, Rubel always managed to stay half a finger's breadth away from capture, and this frustrated the guardsmen so that they sweated and puffed and ran harder still.

Each time around the room, Rubel tried to slip out the door, but each time he always found a flashing sword or a guardsman blocking the way, and so around he went again. And with each revolution, Rubel felt his luck growing more and more impatient to leave, and so at last he made a desperate choice and lunged for the window.

The windows on the top floor of this house opened outward instead of inward, and this was a good thing because Rubel was in far too much of a hurry to care and would have certainly burst out through them just the same, except that this way he didn't get cut by broken glass.

He landed on an adjacent rooftop and the guardsmen nearly fell out of the window in their panic to catch him. Their arms flailed and they shouted things like, "Get back here!" and "Stop You!" neither of which Rubel did.

The Garrison Captain, who's hat had gotten lost somewhere in the fight, didn't stop at the window but pushed his comrades aside and lumbered out on to the sunlit roof. Rubel goggled at the man in the way you goggle at somebody you can outrun, but who isn't at all likely to give up chasing.

The Garrison Captain, his eyes like hot stones, climbed after him.

SKUT
SKAT
CHAK

With his heart pounding, Rubel scrambled up as quickly as he could and dodged across the shingles, trying to keep his head down from the streetside fire. The guardsmen at his back came one after the other out the window and pounded after him, their faces redder and meaner than ever.

To begin with, the situation was thoroughly treacherous. No matter how fast you might be able to run upon a rooftop, even a slow guardsman could keep up with you if he followed along the street where there wasn't any climbing. Indeed, had the situation not changed, Rubel would almost certainly have found himself shot.

But the situation *did* change. The situation filled up with people. At first it was only a few; the normal number for a normal street. But when those few looked to see what the commotion was all about, and when they saw that it was a chase and a fight, they all became very excited and called to their neighbours so that they might see as well. In short order there were people running out from houses and from places far down the street all to follow the spectacle. It got to be so that you almost *did* have to climb. And because the guardsmen were trying to keep up and aim and push people out of their ways all at the same time, they started missing their shots very badly.

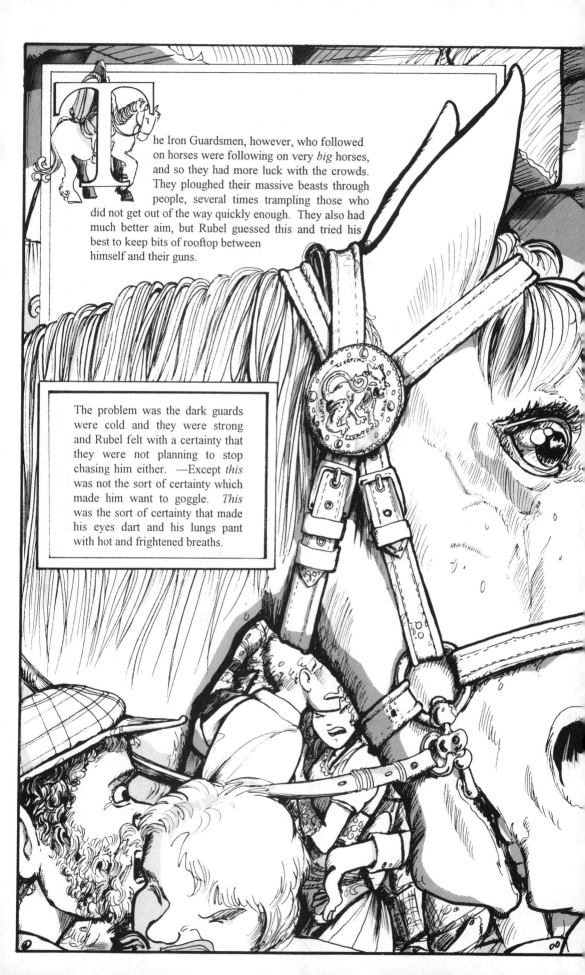

The Iron Guardsmen, however, who followed on horses were following on very *big* horses, and so they had more luck with the crowds. They ploughed their massive beasts through people, several times trampling those who did not get out of the way quickly enough. They also had much better aim, but Rubel guessed this and tried his best to keep bits of rooftop between himself and their guns.

The problem was the dark guards were cold and they were strong and Rubel felt with a certainty that they were not planning to stop chasing him either. —Except *this* was not the sort of certainty which made him want to goggle. *This* was the sort of certainty that made his eyes dart and his lungs pant with hot and frightened breaths.

Even massive horses, however, had their limits. There were simply far too many people filling up streets which were much too narrow to digest such confusion. So trample and stamp as they might, the white beasts of the Iron Guard were soon so thoroughly muddled that they could make no headway, and were left behind like war ships foundering in mud. Further, with the five red faced guardsmen unused to rooftops and unable to run as quickly as Rubel in any case, it began to look all of a sudden as though the boy might just get away. When this realization dawned upon him, Rubel's fright, which had become very tightly wound indeed, loosed all at once, turning into something ticklish and laughing and entirely unexpected.

"HA HA!" he turned and sang, feeling bright and saucy all at once. "YOU CAN'T CATCH ME! YOU CAN'T CATCH ME! I AM THE PRINCESSES' THIEF, I AM!"

And then he ran out of rooftops.

"Nice going," Varkias said, lighting on Rubel's shoulder, still clutching the rose meant for Katara. "I think you should have turned a different way a couple of houses back."

The five guardsmen came puffing up wearing expressions which were quite black.

EASY NOW BOY!

THERE'S NO PLACE TO GO!

NO!

WAIT! WAIT!

HOLD YOUR GUNS!

YOU HEAR ?!

HOLD YOUR GUNS!

PHOO

NOW, LISTEN.

AND I KNOW YOUR IMP CAN'T DO ANY HARM TO US.

YOU ARE IN A LOT OF TROUBLE, AND THERE'S NO WAY YOU'RE GOING TO BE GETTING AROUND THAT!

THERE'S NO MAGIC IN HIM FOR BLINDING, SO IT'S JUST YOU ALL ALONE!

AND I'LL TELL YOU RIGHT NOW THAT I HAVE THE AUTHORITY TO TAKE YOUR LIFE IF I SEE FIT!

I'D JUST AS SOON NOT...

I HAD NO IDEA YOU WERE GOING TO BE SO YOUNG.

I'D JUST AS SOON NOT HAVE TO SPILL YOUR BLOOD...

BUT REGARDLESS OF WHAT I THINK, I CANNOT LET YOU GO.

IF I HAVE TO, THEN I WILL TAKE YOU BACK DEAD.

AND I DON'T MIND TELLING YOU THAT YOU'RE LUCKY YOU MET ME, BECAUSE THERE ARE THOSE WHO'D SEE YOU SHOT WITHOUT QUESTION!

BUT I HAVEN'T DONE ANYTHING.

TRUST ME.

JUST GIVE YOURSELF UP.

HEH.

HE DOESN'T EVEN KNOW!

KNOW WHAT?

THAT YOUR PRINCESS HIDES AND HISSES AT PEOPLE.

AND BITES OFF ANIMAL'S HEADS!

AND SHE SCRATCHED OUT THE EYES OF HER MAID!

AW **C'MON** RUBEL!! DON'T <u>SPARE</u> THEM!

THEY'RE TRYING TO <u>KILL</u> US!! SHOOT ONE GUY AND BASH THE OTH...

QUIET VARKIAS. —THESE MEN ARE JUST SOLDIERS.

BUT THEY ARE THE **PRINCE'S** SOLDIERS!

AND I KNOW ABOUT THE PRINCE!

AND IF I FIND OUT THAT ANYTHING HAS HAPPENED TO KATARA, I WON'T SPARE A SINGLE ONE OF YOU!

<u>NOT</u> <u>ONE!</u>

GALLOP GALLOP GALLO...

Chapter 6

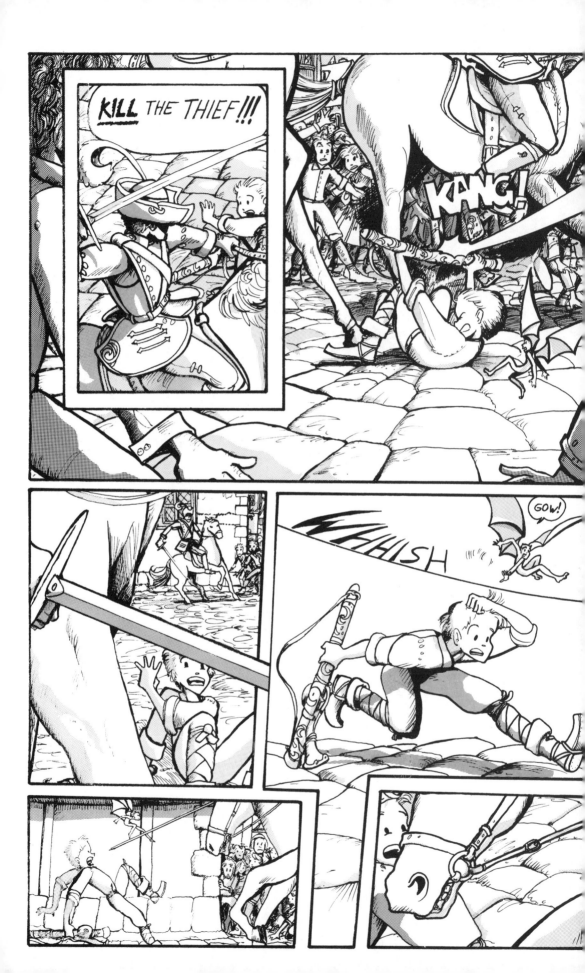

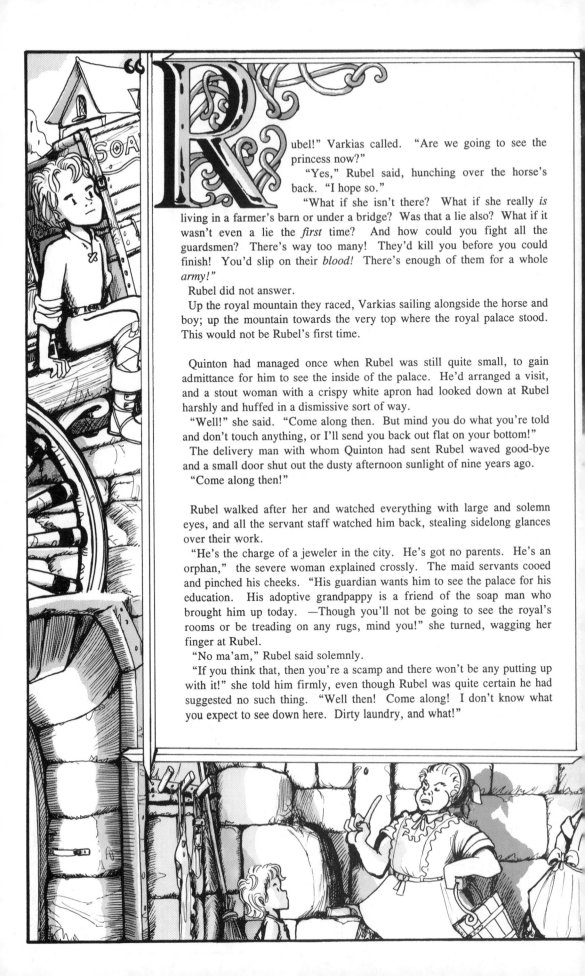

ubel!" Varkias called. "Are we going to see the princess now?"

"Yes," Rubel said, hunching over the horse's back. "I hope so."

"What if she isn't there? What if she really *is* living in a farmer's barn or under a bridge? Was that a lie also? What if it wasn't even a lie the *first* time? And how could you fight all the guardsmen? There's way too many! They'd kill you before you could finish! You'd slip on their *blood!* There's enough of them for a whole *army!*"

Rubel did not answer.

Up the royal mountain they raced, Varkias sailing alongside the horse and boy; up the mountain towards the very top where the royal palace stood. This would not be Rubel's first time.

Quinton had managed once when Rubel was still quite small, to gain admittance for him to see the inside of the palace. He'd arranged a visit, and a stout woman with a crispy white apron had looked down at Rubel harshly and huffed in a dismissive sort of way.

"Well!" she said. "Come along then. But mind you do what you're told and don't touch anything, or I'll send you back out flat on your bottom!"

The delivery man with whom Quinton had sent Rubel waved good-bye and a small door shut out the dusty afternoon sunlight of nine years ago.

"Come along then!"

Rubel walked after her and watched everything with large and solemn eyes, and all the servant staff watched him back, stealing sidelong glances over their work.

"He's the charge of a jeweler in the city. He's got no parents. He's an orphan," the severe woman explained crossly. The maid servants cooed and pinched his cheeks. "His guardian wants him to see the palace for his education. His adoptive grandpappy is a friend of the soap man who brought him up today. —Though you'll not be going to see the royal's rooms or be treading on any rugs, mind you!" she turned, wagging her finger at Rubel.

"No ma'am," Rubel said solemnly.

"If you think that, then you're a scamp and there won't be any putting up with it!" she told him firmly, even though Rubel was quite certain he had suggested no such thing. "Well then! Come along! I don't know what you expect to see down here. Dirty laundry, and what!"

ndeed, they were in a room which seemed very full of laundry; it was the place where all the dirty laundry from the whole castle came to be washed. Piles and piles of it, and girls with their sleeves rolled up scrubbing and beating cloth and blowing out the sides of their mouths. Rubel had seen people clean things before, but never at such a height of industry as this. Huge stone pools carved right there into the floor were filled with water which came from the mouth of a twisting stone dragon built up from the floor; a stone dragon with stone scales shiny from oil and water. Rubel stood quietly to one side, watching the dragon while the poor girls cleaned expensive cloth, until the laundry chamber no longer interested him.

"Could I see the kitchen?" he asked the severe woman, who turned on him with her worst look, trying to frighten him. He returned her glare with the clear eyes of one who does not understand when he is supposed to be frightened, and the servant maidens glanced from one another and laughed into their work, delighted to see their mistress challenged as such.

There were three kitchens, one of which was only used for making bread, and the other two for making everything else. The kitchen master was a big man with enormous arms which looked like legs of ham, and he roared and bellowed and made his underlings scurry about their tasks.

"This is Rubel," the severe woman informed the man. "He's here for his education. He's got no parents and his guardian is a jeweler in the city. He asked if he could see the kitchen."

"Oh Ho!" the man Ho'd, in exactly the way you might expect a cook with ham arms to do.

Rubel looked up at him earnestly.

"I know a bread maker on my friend's street," he told the man. "He chases me sometimes with a rolling pin, but I think his bread isn't that good anyway. I told him he should put sunflower seeds in it, but he said he only makes *good* bread, but I *like* bread with sunflower seeds. What kind of bread does the king like?"

The kitchen master looked at him with astonishment, and laughed again his booming laugh.

"I'll come back for him in a bit," the severe woman advised, exchanging a look with the man.

he kitchen master took an interest in Rubel, and showed him all the various parts of the three kitchens. He showed Rubel the giant bread ovens and he showed him how to chop up a pig into all the right bits, which he did, slapping and turning the meat with his fat palms with such speed and skill Rubel had to gaze in wonder. Then he let Rubel open and close the kitchen windows high up in the vaulted ceiling by using the grand metal hand cranks with their ancient waxy wooden handles. All the kitchen workers paused in their tasks to watch, each remembering when opening and closing the windows was a thrill for them as well and not just another job to do. The kitchen master said that Rubel must come back during the winter to watch the snowflakes fly in and puff into steam upon the oven stones, and sit with his back against a sack of flour with his toes stretched out before the flames with a plate of roast beef drippings in his lap and a pile of hard bread crusts to dip. Rubel said he would like that very much.

He also said that he would like to see the royal stables. The kitchen master escorted him out across a wide yard and into a place where they kept horses and carts and wagons.

The stables were large and interesting, but Rubel had been in places like that before.

"The king's own mount, eh?" the kitchen master and the stable master mused together.

Rubel looked up at them with his gaze honest and unwavering while they mused. The two men talked and then a third man was consulted; a man with a fine collar and expensive buttons and an officer's sword hanging at his belt. This third man stood and listened without saying a word, and he examined Rubel up and down.

"Nothing so special about being an orphan you know," he told Rubel after a long silence.

"It is if you were born in the forest," Rubel told him back. "I'm a thief."

The kitchen master and the stable master both blinked and broke into wide smiles and more, "Oh Ho's!" The officer's eyebrows went up a notch, but he did not smile.

"Oh you are, are you?" he asked quite seriously. "And you think the king would want a thief going over his horses, do you? Knowing how to get in and out? That's quite the education, I'll warrant young man!"

"I wouldn't steal anything from the king," Rubel told him, with equal seriousness. "Not unless he deserved it, and I like the king."

The kitchen master and the stable master watched the officer for his reaction. The officer stroked his chin in thought.

"Fine then," he said, "follow me, but mind you don't misbehave."

Rubel followed the man through a small network of busy streets paved with stones so old they had been worn down, replaced and worn down again, testifying to so many countless generations of palace dwellers passed. They were like streets in a small town, except they went to and fro all right there inside the castle walls. Rubel followed the officer, neither of them speaking a word, crossing by all forms of worker engaged in all forms of work. Up along a curving road they went, which opened out into a real pasture with green grass and hay and blue sky above and more than enough room for a horse to run and play.

Most castles don't have pastures on the inside, but this was the palace at Highborn of Oceansend. There were pastures here, high up so that if you climbed the wall, you could see the city stretching away below and the ocean sparkling beyond. —And you could smell the air, which was fresh and cool even on a summer's day.

"The king has other horses out in the country side, but this one is kept here," the officer nodded toward a chestnut stallion which snorted and stamped before the stable hands. "His father and his father before him were great beasts as well. One of his great, great ancestors, going far back, carried his king into the battle of Corndown. Against the Duke of Corndown. Do you know about that battle?"

Rubel watched the mighty creature stomp about its mountain pasture.

"It's where the Duke kidnapped king Rillion the second's son and armed his soldiers with iron he'd been entrusted with, and then tried to invade the Vale of Sherbeth because of an insult to his sister."

The officer blinked.

"Yes," the man said after a moment, "but that's not the only reason why."

"I know," Rubel said. "Wars never happen for only one reason."

"Quite so."

"If I wanted to meet the king, how would I do it?" Rubel asked, turning to examine the officer's face.

The officer blinked again and didn't know quite how to respond.

Rubel watched him.

"Is there something you want to ask him?"

Rubel thought.

"Not today. But I might one day, and then I would need to know how."

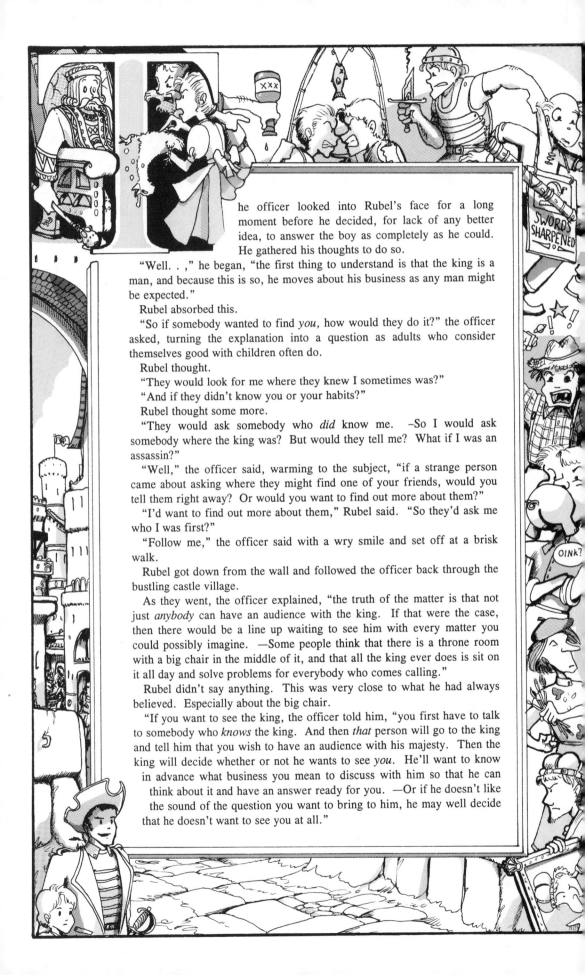

he officer looked into Rubel's face for a long moment before he decided, for lack of any better idea, to answer the boy as completely as he could. He gathered his thoughts to do so.

"Well. . ," he began, "the first thing to understand is that the king is a man, and because this is so, he moves about his business as any man might be expected."

Rubel absorbed this.

"So if somebody wanted to find *you*, how would they do it?" the officer asked, turning the explanation into a question as adults who consider themselves good with children often do.

Rubel thought.

"They would look for me where they knew I sometimes was?"

"And if they didn't know you or your habits?"

Rubel thought some more.

"They would ask somebody who *did* know me. –So I would ask somebody where the king was? But would they tell me? What if I was an assassin?"

"Well," the officer said, warming to the subject, "if a strange person came about asking where they might find one of your friends, would you tell them right away? Or would you want to find out more about them?"

"I'd want to find out more about them," Rubel said. "So they'd ask me who I was first?"

"Follow me," the officer said with a wry smile and set off at a brisk walk.

Rubel got down from the wall and followed the officer back through the bustling castle village.

As they went, the officer explained, "the truth of the matter is that not just *anybody* can have an audience with the king. If that were the case, then there would be a line up waiting to see him with every matter you could possibly imagine. —Some people think that there is a throne room with a big chair in the middle of it, and that all the king ever does is sit on it all day and solve problems for everybody who comes calling."

Rubel didn't say anything. This was very close to what he had always believed. Especially about the big chair.

"If you want to see the king, the officer told him, "you first have to talk to somebody who *knows* the king. And then *that* person will go to the king and tell him that you wish to have an audience with his majesty. Then the king will decide whether or not he wants to see *you*. He'll want to know in advance what business you mean to discuss with him so that he can think about it and have an answer ready for you. —Or if he doesn't like the sound of the question you want to bring to him, he may well decide that he doesn't want to see you at all."

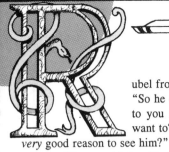

ubel frowned.

"So he doesn't have to talk to you at *all* if he doesn't want to? Even if you have *very* good reason to see him?"

The officer nodded with his wry smile and added, "And sometimes, even if he *would* want to see you, his advisors might not pass your question on to him. Sometimes, if the king doesn't chose his court well, he may find himself surrounded by people who try to do his thinking for him. —Or try not to let him think at all. Sometimes the king is surrounded by people who abuse their power and try to serve their own ends."

Rubel looked up at the officer, squinting.

"So that means," he hazarded, "that even if it was an *emergency* and even if you *had* to talk to him. . . I mean, even if it was *really* important and the king would want to hear you, they might not let you tell him because they might *want* something bad to happen?" His expression was quite suddenly ablaze as the implications of this thought raced several times around the inside of his head.

"Worse than that," the officer added in a hushed voice, "They might even throw you in the dungeon just to keep you from telling! And the king would never even know!"

Rubel chewed his lip and his young and perfect forehead knitted up as he considered. He was taking it all very gravely.

"That's very bad," he declared after a space.

The officer laughed.

"Well yes, except you know, you do have an advantage, if you really are a *thief*. You see here?"

The officer turned about and pointed. They had walked all the way to the massive main gate through which everything leaving or entering the palace had to pass. "If you absolutely needed to get into the palace, all you would have to remember is that during the day, these gates are always open. —Unless, of course, there was a war or something like that going on. For the most part, though, the king relies on his guardsmen watching the entrance. And any thief worth his salt could get in past a few measly guardsmen, don't you think?"

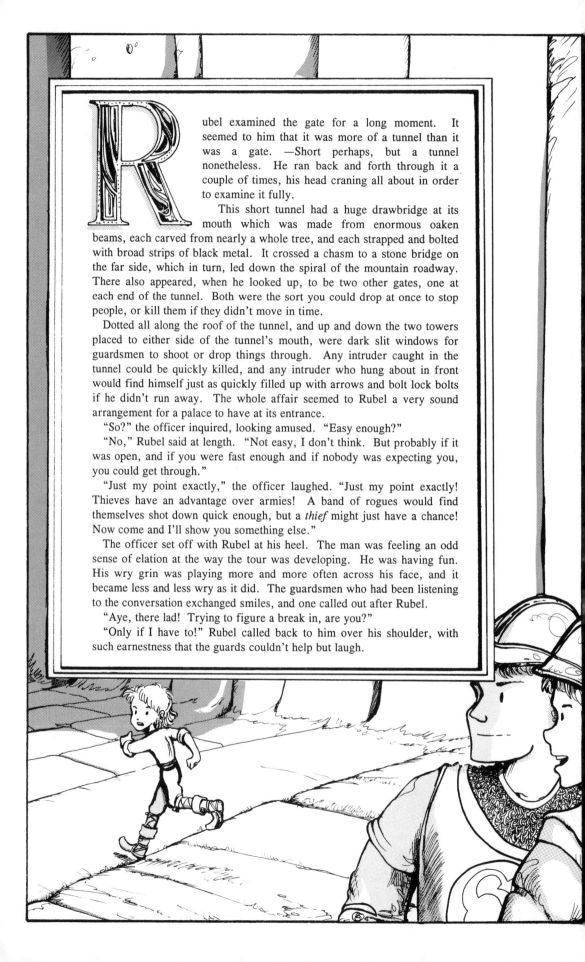

Rubel examined the gate for a long moment. It seemed to him that it was more of a tunnel than it was a gate. —Short perhaps, but a tunnel nonetheless. He ran back and forth through it a couple of times, his head craning all about in order to examine it fully.

This short tunnel had a huge drawbridge at its mouth which was made from enormous oaken beams, each carved from nearly a whole tree, and each strapped and bolted with broad strips of black metal. It crossed a chasm to a stone bridge on the far side, which in turn, led down the spiral of the mountain roadway. There also appeared, when he looked up, to be two other gates, one at each end of the tunnel. Both were the sort you could drop at once to stop people, or kill them if they didn't move in time.

Dotted all along the roof of the tunnel, and up and down the two towers placed to either side of the tunnel's mouth, were dark slit windows for guardsmen to shoot or drop things through. Any intruder caught in the tunnel could be quickly killed, and any intruder who hung about in front would find himself just as quickly filled up with arrows and bolt lock bolts if he didn't run away. The whole affair seemed to Rubel a very sound arrangement for a palace to have at its entrance.

"So?" the officer inquired, looking amused. "Easy enough?"

"No," Rubel said at length. "Not easy, I don't think. But probably if it was open, and if you were fast enough and if nobody was expecting you, you could get through."

"Just my point exactly," the officer laughed. "Just my point exactly! Thieves have an advantage over armies! A band of rogues would find themselves shot down quick enough, but a *thief* might just have a chance! Now come and I'll show you something else."

The officer set off with Rubel at his heel. The man was feeling an odd sense of elation at the way the tour was developing. He was having fun. His wry grin was playing more and more often across his face, and it became less and less wry as it did. The guardsmen who had been listening to the conversation exchanged smiles, and one called out after Rubel.

"Aye, there lad! Trying to figure a break in, are you?"

"Only if I have to!" Rubel called back to him over his shoulder, with such earnestness that the guards couldn't help but laugh.

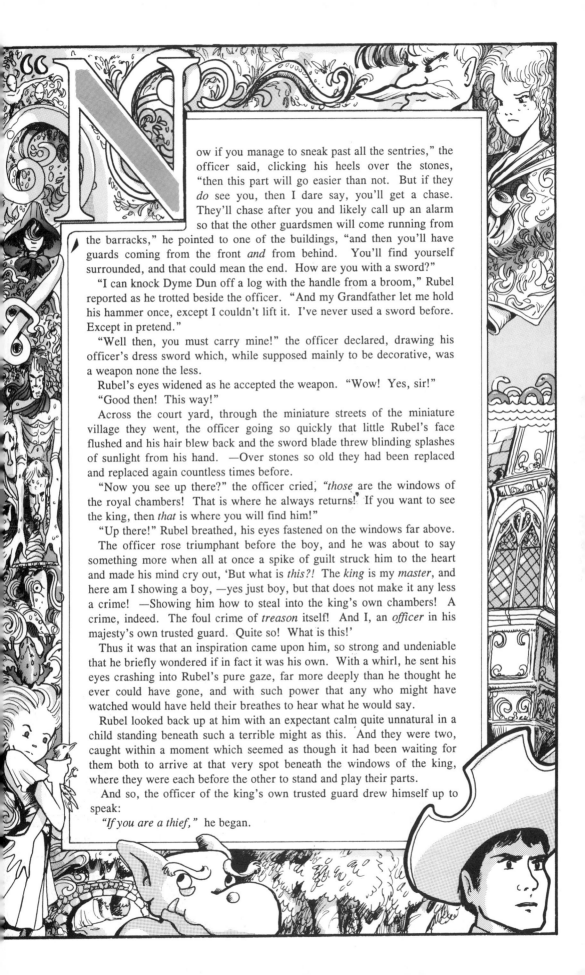

"Now if you manage to sneak past all the sentries," the officer said, clicking his heels over the stones, "then this part will go easier than not. But if they *do* see you, then I dare say, you'll get a chase. They'll chase after you and likely call up an alarm so that the other guardsmen will come running from the barracks," he pointed to one of the buildings, "and then you'll have guards coming from the front *and* from behind. You'll find yourself surrounded, and that could mean the end. How are you with a sword?"

"I can knock Dyme Dun off a log with the handle from a broom," Rubel reported as he trotted beside the officer. "And my Grandfather let me hold his hammer once, except I couldn't lift it. I've never used a sword before. Except in pretend."

"Well then, you must carry mine!" the officer declared, drawing his officer's dress sword which, while supposed mainly to be decorative, was a weapon none the less.

Rubel's eyes widened as he accepted the weapon. "Wow! Yes, sir!"

"Good then! This way!"

Across the court yard, through the miniature streets of the miniature village they went, the officer going so quickly that little Rubel's face flushed and his hair blew back and the sword blade threw blinding splashes of sunlight from his hand. —Over stones so old they had been replaced and replaced again countless times before.

"Now you see up there?" the officer cried, "*those* are the windows of the royal chambers! That is where he always returns! If you want to see the king, then *that* is where you will find him!"

"Up there!" Rubel breathed, his eyes fastened on the windows far above.

The officer rose triumphant before the boy, and he was about to say something more when all at once a spike of guilt struck him to the heart and made his mind cry out, 'But what is *this?!* The *king* is my *master*, and here am I showing a boy, —yes just boy, but that does not make it any less a crime! —Showing him how to steal into the king's own chambers! A crime, indeed. The foul crime of *treason* itself! And I, an *officer* in his majesty's own trusted guard. Quite so! What is this!'

Thus it was that an inspiration came upon him, so strong and undeniable that he briefly wondered if in fact it was his own. With a whirl, he sent his eyes crashing into Rubel's pure gaze, far more deeply than he thought he ever could have gone, and with such power that any who might have watched would have held their breathes to hear what he would say.

Rubel looked back up at him with an expectant calm quite unnatural in a child standing beneath such a terrible might as this. And they were two, caught within a moment which seemed as though it had been waiting for them both to arrive at that very spot beneath the windows of the king, where they were each before the other to stand and play their parts.

And so, the officer of the king's own trusted guard drew himself up to speak:

"*If you are a thief,*" he began.

Last Page of The Story.

Hmm. . .

The opposite page has the final panels of *Thieves & Kings* issue #6, (the comic book), which brings this volume to a close. —With Rubel standing at the lip of the palace draw bridge, wondering what fate awaits him.

A rather annoying place for me to leave you I realize, but hey, I love cliff hangers. Some day, I want to end a comic with Rubel hanging from an actual cliff. I think that would be hilarious.

To be fair, I'll tell you a few things about what you can expect in the next volume:

Let's see. . .

The Shadow Lady comes forward from, er, the shadows, and you get to learn a lot more about her. Also, while Rubel's adventures are only just beginning, he is forced to share some of the spotlight with Quinton, and more importantly, with Quinton's young apprentice, Heath Wingwhit.   —Actually, there's a shot of Heath in this very volume, all grown up, though she's difficult to spot if you haven't been reading further ahead.

As well, the nature of the Iron Guard is partly revealed, and we learn more about both the prince and the king.   There's a whole raft of characters who won't be introduced or properly dealt with until even later volumes.   There's certainly lots to tell. —In fact, the comic books from which these volumes are compiled, were at the time of my writing this, still being published.   Once every two months.   Which means, I suppose, I should probably get back to work.

The Extra Bit

This next piece is a ten page short story which originally appeared in Dave Sim's *Cerebus* in the form of a preview. It's only ten pages long, very hastily produced, and bears what is probably the worst dangling end of any story I've ever written, so I'll apologize in advance. I've reprinted it here because a first trade paperback, I think, calls for something a little extra. —And also because the princess gets hardly any page space at all in the first ten or twenty issues, which is too bad; Katara's story is a really good one, which I'm sure could easily stand on its own.

Still, I'll get to her eventually. All in good time. For now though, this piece gives a few well deserved hints as to Katara's whereabouts. Keep in mind that this scene took place some time ago. —A few months after Rubel and Katara first met in the forest and made their pact. About three and a half years ago.

Ladies and Gentlemen, *The Crossing*.

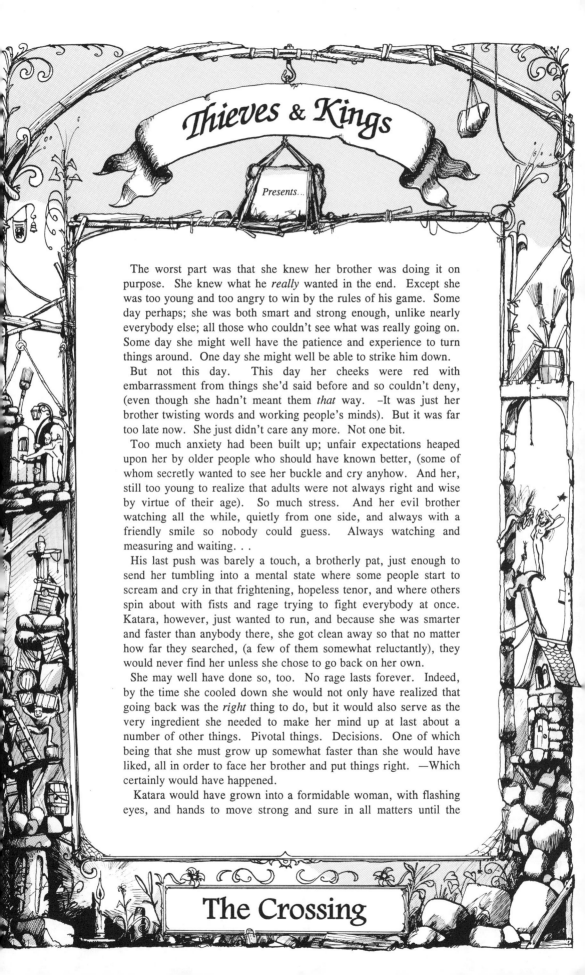

The worst part was that she knew her brother was doing it on purpose. She knew what he *really* wanted in the end. Except she was too young and too angry to win by the rules of his game. Some day perhaps; she was both smart and strong enough, unlike nearly everybody else; all those who couldn't see what was really going on. Some day she might well have the patience and experience to turn things around. One day she might well be able to strike him down.

But not this day. This day her cheeks were red with embarrassment from things she'd said before and so couldn't deny, (even though she hadn't meant them *that* way. –It was just her brother twisting words and working people's minds). But it was far too late now. She just didn't care any more. Not one bit.

Too much anxiety had been built up; unfair expectations heaped upon her by older people who should have known better, (some of whom secretly wanted to see her buckle and cry anyhow. And her, still too young to realize that adults were not always right and wise by virtue of their age). So much stress. And her evil brother watching all the while, quietly from one side, and always with a friendly smile so nobody could guess. Always watching and measuring and waiting. . .

His last push was barely a touch, a brotherly pat, just enough to send her tumbling into a mental state where some people start to scream and cry in that frightening, hopeless tenor, and where others spin about with fists and rage trying to fight everybody at once. Katara, however, just wanted to run, and because she was smarter and faster than anybody there, she got clean away so that no matter how far they searched, (a few of them somewhat reluctantly), they would never find her unless she chose to go back on her own.

She may well have done so, too. No rage lasts forever. Indeed, by the time she cooled down she would not only have realized that going back was the *right* thing to do, but it would also serve as the very ingredient she needed to make her mind up at last about a number of other things. Pivotal things. Decisions. One of which being that she must grow up somewhat faster than she would have liked, all in order to face her brother and put things right. —Which certainly would have happened.

Katara would have grown into a formidable woman, with flashing eyes, and hands to move strong and sure in all matters until the

The Crossing

world would come to both fear her and love her above all else.
Except in the Sleeping Wood, angry, tearful states like hers were
nearly always the keys for unlocking *other* things. . . The Sleeping
Wood, at the mouth of which her brother had insisted the picnic be
held. . .

The Wood felt her darting beneath its boughs; a tiny bundle of fury
and sadness and loneliness which made its roots ache as she
passed. Though while it had little patience for such
things, it did have a place to keep them, deep within its
magic gut where uncompromising creatures could be
digested and quietly forgotten. And so, with grumbling
nudges and shifting roots, Katara's blind race was
diverted along hidden pathways and secret trails until
she was far away from where she had begun, and far
more lost than she could begin to understand. . .

!?

HEY!!

JUST WHERE DO YOU THINK YOU'RE GOING ?!

HMM?

I'M, UM, I...

I MEAN, I'M JUST..

I'M GOING TO THE OTHER SIDE.

WHAT OF IT?

WHAT OF IT?!

THIS IS <u>MY</u> BRIDGE!!

<u>THAT'S</u> <u>WHAT</u> <u>OF</u> IT!

AND YOU CAN'T CROSS IT UNTIL YOU ANSWER MY RIDDLE!

WHAT DO YOU THINK OF <u>THAT</u>?!

YOUR RIDDLE?

THAT'S <u>RIGHT</u>! AND IF YOU GET IT WRONG, I GET TO EAT YOU UP!

SOME TROLLS JUST MAKE YOU GO AWAY, BUT <u>I</u> EAT UP ANYONE WHO CAN'T ANSWER MY RIDDLE. —AND DON'T THINK YOU CAN RUN AWAY OR ANYTHING. —I MAY LOOK SLOW, BUT I'M FASTER THAN A HORSE!

YOU'RE A <u>TROLL</u>?

DARN TOOTIN' I AM!

WHAT DO <u>I</u> LOOK LIKE?

A <u>CHIPMUNK</u>?

I DON'T KNOW. I'VE NEVER—

SAVE IT.

JUST LISTEN TO THE RIDDLE, —AND LISTEN CAREFUL.

I ONLY SAY IT <u>ONCE</u>.

I GET TO EAT YOU UP THEN.

IF YOU RENEGE ON THE RIDDLE, I GET TO EAT YOU UP.

I DON'T CARE.

YOU GOING TO TRY AND RUN AWAY?

WHAT'S THE POINT IF YOU'RE FASTER THAN ME?

I'LL TRY AND FIGHT YOU THOUGH.

—I BET I COULD GRAB THAT EAR-RING AND TEAR A BIG GASH IN YOUR EAR LOBE BEFORE YOU COULD EAT ME UP.

—I MIGHT EVEN BE ABLE TO POKE OUT ONE OF YOUR EYES.

ER.., AHM...

WELL, YOU KNOW..,

UM...

IF YOU WANTED...

The End